DEEP SPACE

DEEP SPACE

THE UNIVERSE FROM THE BEGINNING

STUART CLARK

Quercus

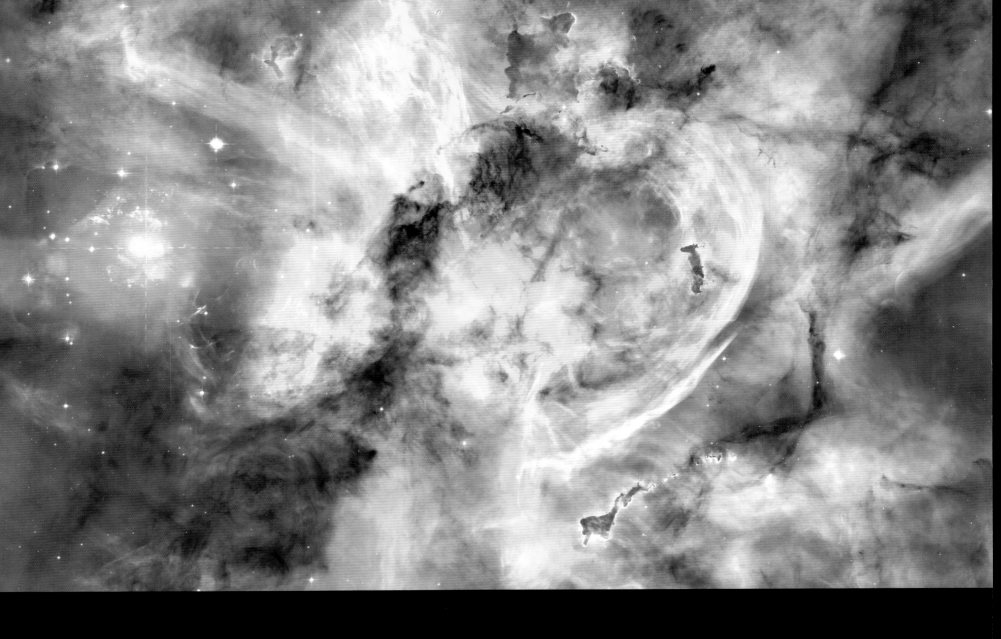

CONTENTS

INTRODUCTION 6

01 GALAXIES LIKE GRAINS OF SAND 10

02 ANATOMY OF A GALAXY 36

03 THE ORDER OF THE UNIVERSE 70

04 THE EXPANDING UNIVERSE AND THE BIG BANG 88

05 GRAVITY – ARCHITECT OF THE UNIVERSE 104

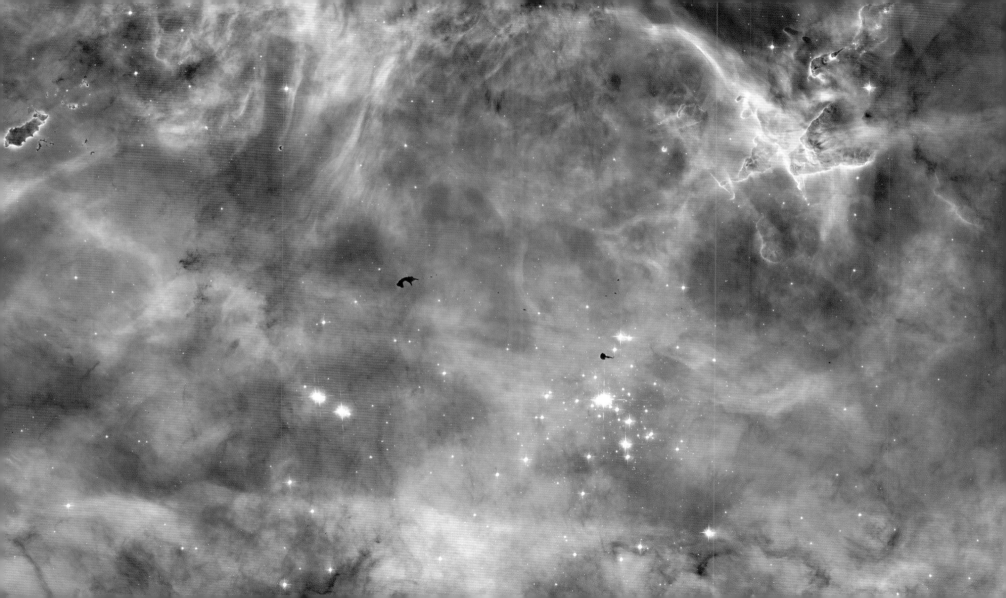

This is a journey into both deep space and the science of cosmology. Intimately related to astronomy, cosmology concerns itself with the universe as a whole. Whereas astronomers study the individual celestial objects, attempting to determine their composition and behaviour, cosmologists think about the bigger picture. They want to know where the universe came from, how it came to be the way it is today and what will happen to it in the future. There is literally no larger field of scientific study.

Cosmology in its modern form began in the early decades of the 20th century. This was when Edwin Hubble showed that the galaxies were not small clouds of stars within the Milky Way, but vast cities of stars far beyond the boundaries of our galaxy. In addition, Hubble showed that the universe itself was expanding. The other work crucial to cosmology was Albert Einstein's theory of general relativity. This proved essential because it could be used to describe the way the universe expands.

In the quest to understand the universe, the work of the cosmologist takes place beyond the planets of the solar system, beyond even the stars in the night sky. Cosmologists find their inspiration in the distant realm of the galaxies. Each is home to between a few hundred million to a trillion stars, and sits like a remote island, separated from its nearest neighbour by vast tracts of almost empty space.

Astronomers provide the knowledge about what galaxies are and how they behave; cosmologists use the galaxies as the smallest building blocks with which to trace the evolution of the universe.

Stretches of space

The distances that astronomers and cosmologists have to work with are vast. To help them cope, astronomers have defined the light year. It is simply the distance that light can travel in a year. Light is the fastest thing in the universe, travelling 299,792,458 metres (186,288 miles) every second, so in one year it can cross approximately 9.5 trillion km (5.9 trillion miles). This concept makes life easier when referring to and comparing celestial distances. For example, the Andromeda Galaxy is 22 million trillion km (13.6 million trillion miles) or 2.3 million light years away.

Referring to distances in light years also allows astronomers and cosmologists to be aware of the 'look-back time' to a celestial object. On everyday scales, light travels so quickly that to all intents and purposes it can be thought of as travelling instantaneously from one place to another. In the universe at large, however, the distances are so vast that light can take millions or even billions of years to cross them. So, when astronomers collect light through their telescopes to produce an image, they are not seeing a celestial object as it appears today; instead they are seeing it as it looked when that light was emitted. The distance in light years instantly tells you how far back in time the object is located. For example, a star that is a thousand light years away, appears as it did a thousand years ago.

In normal astronomy, the lifespan of celestial objects is so large that this does not make much difference. In cosmology, however, distances of

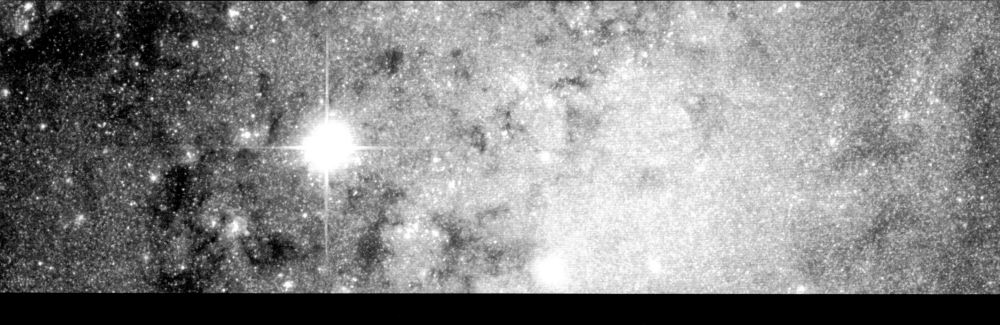

hundreds of millions or even billions of light years mean that cosmologists have to be aware that they are looking at the object not as it exists today but as it existed a long time ago. So, a galaxy located two million light years distant cannot be easily compared with one at two billion light years. In the intervening time, galaxies might have changed dramatically.

Far from being a nuisance, look-back time is one of the key concepts that make cosmology possible. By looking further and further into space, cosmologists can compare the galaxies at various distances and see how their characteristics have evolved over time.

Light of many colours

Traditionally, we think of astronomers peering out into space through telescopes that collect the light from these distant realms. Light is only one small part of the broader electromagnetic spectrum, however. Our eyes are sensitive to electromagnetic rays with wavelengths of a few hundred billionths of a metre, or yard. Nowadays, modern instrumentation can collect many other types of electromagnetic rays that are invisible to our eyes: gamma-rays, X-rays, ultraviolet, infrared, microwaves and radio.

Optical or visible radiation sits between the ultraviolet and infrared regions of the spectrum, with ultraviolet radiation having shorter wavelengths and infrared longer. To display these images so that we can see them, the information is colour-coded by computers. This is often known as false colour and there are several places where it is used in this book. By looking at the universe through these electronic eyes, astronomers and cosmologists harvest a wealth of information that would otherwise have been inaccessible.

However, there are parts of the universe that may always remain invisible to us. As astronomers and cosmologists have become better at measuring the movement of galaxies, so they have come to believe that vast quantities of extra mass must exist in the universe. This so-called dark matter is unlike any other form of matter we know today. Physicists conjecture that it may be a 'relic', a species of particle that was important in the early universe where temperatures, energies and densities were much higher but that now simply clumps in space, reacting with almost nothing except by generating a gravitational field. Because it interacts so weakly, it cannot be seen with normal telescopes, yet its gravitational influence holds galaxies and clusters of galaxy together. Estimates suggest that the dark matter outweighs normal matter by over ten times.

As extraordinary as this sounds, cosmologists currently believe that a different 'dark component' outweighs even this. Dark energy, as they call it, is causing the universe to expand faster and faster. By modern estimates, dark energy constitutes 74 percent of the universe, leaving 22 percent dark matter, and 4 percent ordinary matter.

From our vantage point, on a small planet, orbiting a small star in the outer reaches of a galaxy called the Milky Way, astronomers gaze at the distant realms of the universe in awe and wonder. Within these pages, you can look through their eyes, and glimpse the exotic realms of deep space.

Stuart Clark

GALAXIES LIKE GRAINS OF SAND

GALAXIES ARE THE KEYS WITH WHICH TO UNLOCK THE
UNIVERSE. EACH IS AN ENORMOUS COLLECTION OF
STARS, BOUND TOGETHER BY GRAVITY. THE BIGGEST
CONTAIN AROUND TEN TRILLION STARS, WHEREAS
THE SMALLEST PLAY HOST TO 'JUST' A FEW TENS OF
MILLIONS.

   ASTRONOMERS ESTIMATE THAT THERE ARE PROBABLY
MORE THAN ONE HUNDRED BILLION GALAXIES IN THE
UNIVERSE, MORE THAN THE TYPICAL NUMBER OF SAND
GRAINS ON A BEACH.

Galaxies like grains of sand

EO   E3   E7   SO

Each galaxy is an individual, unique in its appearance and properties. Nevertheless, they can be broadly classified according to their shape, the three main types being spiral, barred spiral and elliptical; others are lenticular (shaped like a lens), irregular and ring galaxies. Spirals are particularly beautiful, with sweeping arms of burning blue stars surrounding a central bulge of ageing yellow stars. Barred spirals are similar but with a straight bar of stars that connects the central bulge to the spiral arms. Ellipticals are radically different in appearance – from perfect spheres to stretched ovals through to long spindles – and are often much larger than the spiral or barred spiral galaxies.

Types of galaxy

Understanding why galaxies take these particular shapes has been a preoccupation of astronomers for almost a century, ever since telescopes became powerful enough to show them in detail. We now understand that a galaxy's shape is a window onto its past. Spirals have rested undisturbed in space for many millions, possibly even billions, of years. Elliptical galaxies have had a more violent history, crashing into other galaxies and, in some cases, swelling up to an enormous size.

The very largest ellipticals tend to be found resting at the centre of vast clusters of galaxies. They are thought to have built up through successive mergers of all types of galaxies, as they were drawn into the heart of the cluster.

Spirals and barred spirals account for about three-quarters of all large, bright galaxies, with all of the other types making up the remainder. However, there are vast numbers of smaller elliptical and irregular galaxies spread across the universe. We refer to these smaller systems as dwarf galaxies and when they are also taken into account the proportions reverse, so that the fraction of spirals drops to around 25 percent.

Dwarf galaxies might span just a few thousand light years, whereas a typical spiral stretches across 100,000 light years of space. In the case of the most massive ellipticals, they can encompass five million light years.

Astronomers are increasingly turning their attention to the irregular galaxies. These are a subset of the galaxies that defy classification

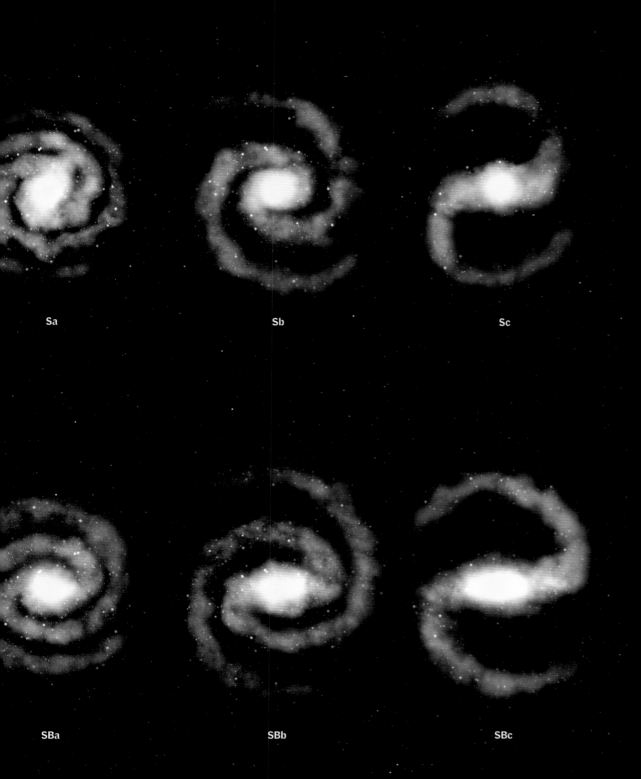

Sa   Sb   Sc

SBa   SBb   SBc

The Hubble tuning fork diagram

Only in the early decades of the 20th century did astronomers finally succeed in building telescopes large enough to see the galaxies in detail. In 1926, using the 100-inch Hale telescope at the Carnegie Institution's Mount Wilson Observatory, near Pasadena, California, American astronomer Edwin Hubble developed a way to classify galaxies.

Based on his observations, he concluded that there were three main types of galaxies: spiral, barred spiral and elliptical, which he then subdivided. For the ellipticals he divided them according to how perfectly round they were: E0 galaxies are spherical while E7 are highly elongated. Spirals and barred spirals were split and further classified according to how tightly their arms were wound. Those galaxies with the tightest windings are known as Sa and SBa. Those with the loosest arms are Sc and SBc.

There were two other types as well: lenticular (S0) and irregular. Hubble thought the lenticular galaxies were somehow intermediate between the spirals and the ellipticals and concluded that the irregulars were fundamentally unclassifiable.

into the spiral or elliptical camps. We now realize that these particular galaxies have been disturbed in some way during the relatively recent past. In some cases, they have been virtually torn apart, allowing us to peer inside a galaxy in a way that would not usually be possible.

The other way to classify galaxies, in addition to by shape, is by whether they are still actively forming stars. In general, spiral, barred spiral and irregular galaxies are star-forming. Elliptical and lenticular galaxies are sterile systems, consisting only of ageing stars.

Our galaxy

Our own solar system, consisting of the Sun and its planets, sits in a galaxy called the Milky Way. It is a barred spiral and contains every

star that can be seen from Earth with the naked eye and a hundred billion more that are too faint to observe without a telescope. The name Milky Way refers to the misty band of light that stretches across the night-time sky. This is the collected light of the millions of stars that reside in our galaxy but are too far away to be seen as individual stars, instead merging into a faint band.

Galileo Galilei was the first person to record observations of the night sky under magnification. In 1609, he looked at the Milky Way with a telescope that possessed a lens just two inches across. He was amazed to see the band transform into a countless number of individual stars. Since then, with every improvement in telescopes and observational techniques, astronomers have learnt more about the universe.

Trapped inside the disc of the Milky Way, we have no way of actually seeing the shape of our galaxy. It must be a thin system because the Milky Way is a narrow band of light that stretches across the sky. This means it must be a kind of spiral galaxy. By charting the speed of gas clouds around the centre of the Milky Way, astronomers found evidence that it has several large spiral arms that wind loosely from the central regions to the outer edges, as well as a few smaller spurs. Our solar system sits in one of these, called the Orion spur.

Perhaps the most interesting discovery about the Milky Way in recent years is that it has a small bar of stars connecting its central bulge of stars to its spiral arms. Even our own galaxy can still surprise us.

MYRIAD GALAXIES

GALAXY SURVEY IN URSA MAJOR

50,000 galaxies on a celestial pinhead

To the naked eye, most of the night sky looks dark and empty. However, with a telescope, the universe opens up. This thin strip of dark sky near the Big Dipper (the Plough), right, in the northern constellation of Ursa Major, contains over 50,000 individual galaxies, revealed for the first time in these Hubble Space Telescope pictures (top and far right).

The thin strip covers about the same amount of sky as the silhouette of your finger held at arm's length. It is about the length of two full moons, but not as wide. Most of the galaxies in this image are young, just three or four billion years old. In human terms they would be children aged ten and above. The largest, most well-formed, can be thought of as young adults.

These largest galaxies already have well-defined shapes and look similar to their fully mature cousins seen closer to the Earth. Most of the galaxies in this image, however, are little more than irregularly shaped stellar smudges containing a few million stars. Many of these will eventually collide, coalescing into larger forms, although some will remain forever as dwarf galaxies.

We estimate that there are one hundred billion galaxies spread across the observable universe.

SPIRAL GALAXIES

M101 THE PINWHEEL GALAXY

Staring a galaxy in the face

All spirals display the same basic pattern and
the Pinwheel Galaxy is perhaps the archetypal
form. At its centre is a great bulge of long-lived
stars. Each can exist for billions of years and
their combined slow-burn radiation shines into
space as a golden yellow colour.

Moving beyond the galactic bulge, a flatter
disc of stars surrounds this great mass. Clusters
of short-lived stars shine with a brilliant blue
intensity, marking out spiral arms. Blue stars
race through their lifecycles in just a few
million years.

Even by galactic standards, the Pinwheel
Galaxy is a giant. At nearly twice the size of our
own Milky Way, it spans 170,000 light years and
contains an estimated trillion stars. It also plays
host to a small group of other galaxies, each
bound to one another by the force of their
mutual gravitational fields.

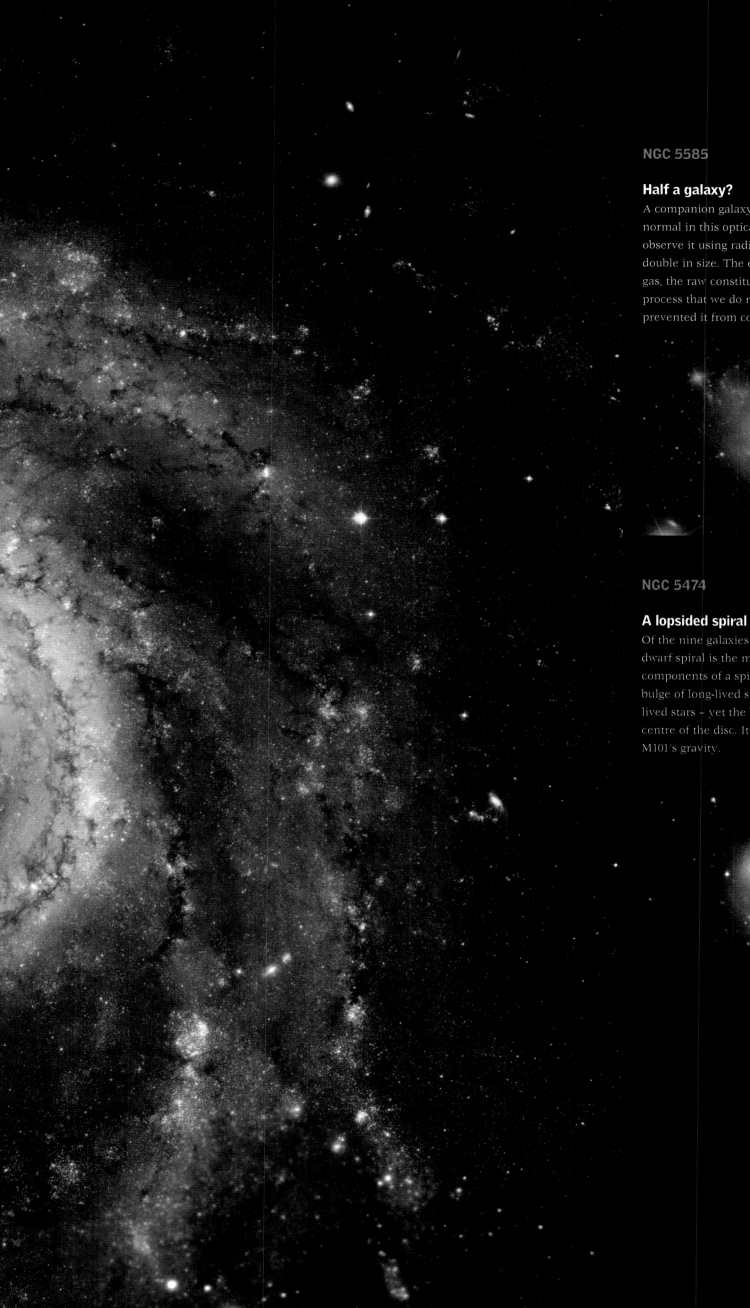

NGC 5585

Half a galaxy?

A companion galaxy to M101, NGC 5585 look[s]
normal in this optical picture. However, if we
observe it using radio telescopes it appears to
double in size. The extra material is hydroge[n]
gas, the raw constituent of new stars. Some
process that we do not yet understand has
prevented it from collapsing into stars.

NGC 5474

A lopsided spiral

Of the nine galaxies that belong to M101, this
dwarf spiral is the most peculiar. It has all the
components of a spiral galaxy – the central
bulge of long-lived stars and the disc of short-
lived stars – yet the bulge does not sit in the
centre of the disc. It is being distorted by
M101's gravity.

GRAND DESIGNS vs FLOCCULENT SPIRALS

M51 THE WHIRLPOOL GALAXY

A grand design of star formation

There are two subtly different spiral patterns that are seen in galaxies. Both are thought to result from the dominant way in which stars form in that particular galaxy.

In the case of M51, two dominant spiral arms can be traced from the centre of the galaxy. We call this a grand design spiral. It is caused by a rippling wave in the density of matter as the spiral arms sweep around the centre of the galaxy. These ripples compress dust and gas as they pass by, triggering star formation. This image has been enhanced to show the dark dust lanes that will become stars and the red bubbles of hot gas that reveal the stellar birthplaces.

NGC 4414

The messy whorl of star formation

In contrast to the grand design of M51, this galaxy is a messy whorl of star formation. It is known as a flocculent spiral and its appearance is the result of a different process for making stars. In this case, star formation proceeds on its own, with little intervention from density waves rippling around the galaxy.

As each cluster of bright stars forms, those stars closest to the centre of the galaxy orbit faster, while those further out move more slowly. This stretches out star-forming regions into truncated spirals patterns. Thousands of these little arcs contribute to the woolly appearance of a flocculent galaxy.

THIN BANDS OF STARS

NGC 4013

An edge-on spiral galaxy

Spiral galaxies are relatively thin objects. Although they can span over 100,000 light years in diameter, the thickness of their spiral arms is often little more than a hundredth of this. In this image of NGC 4013, we can appreciate just how thin it really is.

Edge-on spirals reveal the dust lanes that orbit them. These can be so thick that they seem to cut the galaxy in half and are composed of an uncountable number of dust grains, most of them smaller than a millionth of a metre, or yard, in diameter.

At 55 million light years away, this galaxy's stars are not seen as single objects, but instead appear to merge into a misty mass of light. By comparison, the extremely bright star in the upper left of the image, and the others that dot the image, lie in our own Milky Way and just happen to be in the foreground.

ESO510-G13

A warped spiral galaxy

The disc of this particular spiral is markedly
warped. We believe that this has been caused
by a collision with a much smaller galaxy. Any
collision will stimulate a burst of star formation
that will transform the dark dust lanes into
blazing trails of stars.

NGC 3370

A tilted spiral galaxy

This spiral has its lower edge tipped towards us
and so appears flattened from top to bottom.
Imagine tipping the galaxy all the way up, so
that it appears edge-on to us. NGC 3370 would
then appear similar to the more distant galaxy
in the bottom right of the image. The blue stars
of the spiral disc cannot be seen so easily but
the shape of the central bulge, with its yellow
stars, is more readily appreciated.

LENTICULAR
GALAXIES

The Sombrero Galaxy

Some galaxies look as though they should be
spirals but they lack any arms. The Sombrero
Galaxy is a perfect example. It is edge-on with
a dominant dust lane but the spiral arms are
missing. We call such galaxies lenticular
because they bear a passing resemblance to
the shape of an optical lens.

The Sombrero Galaxy contains an estimated
800 billion stars, most of them clustered
together in the dense central bulge that
stretches 50,000 light years in diameter.
We are not sure what causes a galaxy to lose
its spiral arms. It might be that it has used up
most of its star-forming gas, or it may be that
the density waves that drive the spiral arms
have simply died away.

Infrared

Through different eyes

By switching from optical telescopes to observations at infrared or X-ray wavelengths, the same object can appear quite different. Infrared radiation comes from cooler objects than optical emissions, so in this light (far left) most of the 800 billion stars vanish. In contrast, the cool dust lanes that appear in silhouette in the optical image suddenly become bright.

Viewed through an X-ray telescope (left), the dust lanes disappear and hot gas shows up.

X-ray

LIMBLESS
LENSES

NGC 2787

A face-on lenticular galaxy

If the Sombrero Galaxy were turned face-on to us, this is what it would look like. NGC 2787 has a distinctive central bulge, surrounded by a thin disc of more stars. However there are no spiral arms in the disc, just concentric lanes of dust.

NGC 2787 lies roughly 24 million light years away from Earth. We are not sure whether star formation could be restarted in a lenticular galaxy. Many of them appear to contain large quantities of dust but not so much gas. Perhaps if another galaxy happened to pass close by, its gravity would stir the lenticular back into action.

M84

Lenticular or not?

Sometimes the classification of galaxies is difficult. For many years M84 was classified as elliptical. Now, however, we are wondering whether it is actually a face-on lenticular galaxy. It sits near the centre of a large cluster of galaxies, in the constellation of Virgo.

BARRED SPIRALS

NGC 1300

Arms across a galaxy

Barred spirals display all the same attributes as a spiral galaxy – the bulge of long-lived yellow stars, the arms of short-lived blue stars, the dark lanes of dust – but the arms are connected to the bulge by a straight bar of stars.

We now estimate that up to 80 percent of all spiral galaxies possess a straight bar of stars or dusty material that runs between their central bulge and their spiral arms.

However, most are not as impressive as the stunning NGC 1300. It lies 75 million light years away and has been studied extensively in order to deduce how galactic bars form. We believe that a bar develops when the orbits of stars and gas clouds fall into step, and reinforce each other.

According to computer simulations, bars are not a constant feature of any individual spiral. Instead, they seem to be able to form and subsequently disperse throughout a galaxy's lifetime.

The heart of NGC 1300 holds a surprise. Zooming in on the central region shows a miniature version of a grand design spiral galaxy. Stretching just 3300 light years across, the small grand design can be seen as spiral lanes of dust, intermixed with brilliant arms of stars. We have observed similar features in the heart of several of the largest barred spirals.

GRASPING ARMS

NGC 1672

Feeding the monster

The bars in a spiral act as channels for dust and gas to lose energy and fall into the centre of the galaxy. Once there, the raw material can either go on to become a new generation of stars or it can feed a supermassive black hole at the very heart. This latter option seems to be the case for NGC 1672 because we can detect the restless activity of a feeding monster right at the galaxy's centre.

NGC 6782

Ring of fire

This barred spiral also holds a surprise. It has a ring of fiery stars that can be seen surrounding the nucleus and differentiating the bar region from the spiral arms. This particular view of NGC 6782 is a combination of optical and ultraviolet images. The ring of newly formed stars only shows up in ultraviolet wavelengths and was originally missed by astronomers working only with optical telescopes.

HCG 87

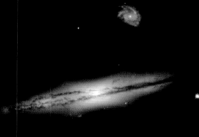

The peanut feature

This edge-on galaxy is thought to be a barred spiral. The give-away characteristic is that the nucleus is no longer lens-shaped. Instead it more closely resembles a peanut shell. Such a distortion is seen to occur in computer models that simulate bar formation in galaxies. As most stars fall into step with one another to form the bar, others have their orbits tilted, creating the peanut shape.

ELLIPTICAL GALAXIES

Dusty elliptical galaxy

Ellipticals are round masses of stars that can grow to gigantic proportions. The largest are found at the centre of clusters of galaxies, where it is thought that many galaxies have fallen together and merged into a single, giant system. Ellipticals are usually yellow in colour, signifying that there is little or no star formation taking place within.

This particular elliptical is more than 120,000 light years across and is called NGC 1316. Unusually, it contains obvious clouds of dust. We think that it must be relatively young and was formed sometime in the last few hundred million years from the collision of two other galaxies. Eventually, in another billion years, the dust will have dispersed throughout the galaxy and it will resemble a typical, featureless elliptical.

M32

Small and dense

At the other end of the scale, M32 is a relatively small elliptical. Spanning only 1000 light years, it contains just 400 million stars and is relatively close to us, only 2.3 million light years away.

This image highlights the central section of M32, only 175 light years across. The way the brightness rises to a point shows how crowded the galaxy becomes. In the very centre, we estimate that stars are packed in at over 100 million times the density of stars in the Sun's neighbourhood. At night time, a planet around one of these stars would see the sky glowing from the other stars with a brightness a hundred times greater than our Moon.

IRREGULAR
AND DWARF
GALAXIES

LARGE MAGELLANIC CLOUD

Nearby neighbour

The nearest galaxies to the Milky Way are
irregular in shape. This image is of the Large
Magellanic Cloud, a collection of stars lying just
179,000 light years away. It can be seen with
the naked eye in the southern sky as an
elongated patch of misty light. The Persian
astronomer Abd al-Rahman al Suf mentioned
the Large Magellanic Cloud in his *Book of Fixed
Stars* that dates from AD 964. He called it Al
Bakr, the White Ox.

    The Large Magellanic Cloud contains some
extremely active regions of star formation, seen
here as pink wisps, perhaps triggered by the
gravitational influence of the Milky Way.

NGC 4214

Celestial conflagration

Clouds of dust and gas fuel a massive bout of
star formation taking place in this irregular
galaxy. NGC 4214 has a diameter of 22,000 light
years and is located 8 million light years away.

NGC 1569

Irregular galaxy

This galaxy, 7 million light years away, has
been driven into an irregular shape by a close
gravitational encounter with another galaxy.
The near miss also triggered a bout of vigorous
star formation that has swept across NGC 1569,
engulfing its 10,000 light years' diameter.

NGC 4449

Bar of stars

This dwarf galaxy is little more than a bar of
stars, stretching through space. Although a
dwarf galaxy when viewed with an optical
telescope, there is much more to it than meets
the eye. At radio wavelengths, a shell of
hydrogen gas, fourteen times larger than the
visible portions of the galaxy, is revealed.

NGC 1427A

A galaxy being ripped apart

Many galaxies, mostly the smaller ones, have
no set shape. Instead, they are simply messy
conglomerations of stars. We call these the
irregular galaxies and NGC 1427A is a good
example. It lies in the Fornax cluster of
galaxies, some 60 million light years away.

NGC 1427A is richly stocked with gas – the
raw ingredient to make stars – and the bright
blue knots of stars show that star formation is
ongoing. Studies of the way stars move within
this galaxy suggest that it is being torn in half
by the gravity of other, larger galaxies in the
cluster. Within a few hundred million years,
this tug of war will pull NGC 1427A apart and
scatter its stars throughout the cluster.

RING GALAXIES

HOAG'S OBJECT

A perfect circle

Hoag's object is a beautiful mystery. An almost
perfect circle of young stars surrounding a core
of older ones, we call it a ring galaxy for
obvious reasons. Such structures are the rarest
form of galaxy in the universe.

Ordinarily, we would assume that a smaller
galaxy had plunged through the heart of Hoag's
object, setting up shock waves that have
radiated outwards just like the ripples on a
pond caused by a dropped stone. The collision
is thought to have taken place between three
and four billion years ago. The trouble is, there
is no sign of the intruder anywhere in the
image. So what hit the galaxy? Has the intruder
been completely absorbed? Some astronomers
have suggested that it might have once been a
barred spiral, whose bar collapsed and left a
ring of stars.

By a peculiar coincidence, another ring
galaxy can be seen just above and slightly to
the right of Hoag's nucleus. It appears smaller
because it is much further away than Hoag's
galaxy, which lies 600 million light years from
Earth.

The space between the ring of blue stars
and the nucleus of yellow stars could contain
some star clusters, but they are too faint to be
seen on this image.

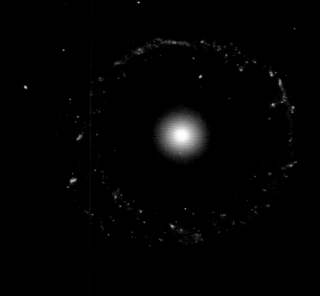

ESO 350-G40

Cartwheel Galaxy

The Cartwheel Galaxy is another example of a
ring galaxy, this time at 500 million light years.
The impacting galaxy was the irregular galaxy
seen to the side of the Cartwheel, having passed
straight through. Computer processing reveals
the ghostly glow of spiral arms in the dark
space inside the ring. We are not sure whether
these are the last vestiges of previously glorious
spiral arms or the first signs of them reasserting
themselves after being wiped out by the collision.

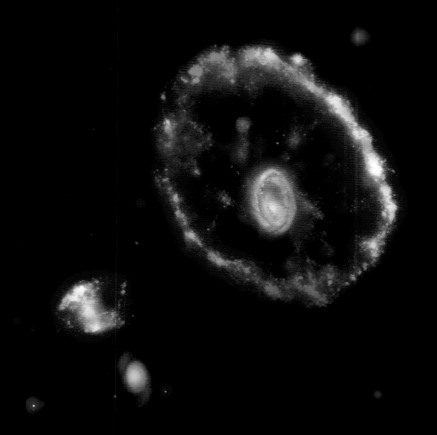

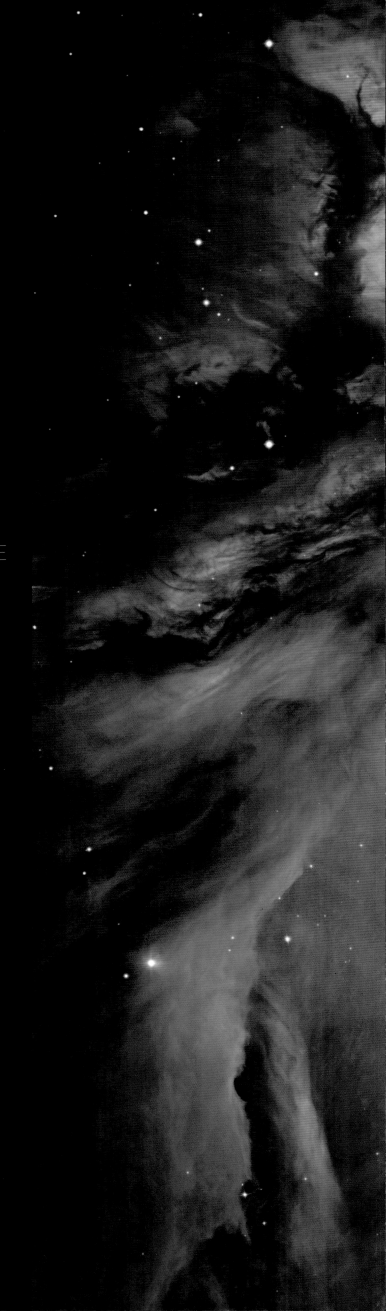

ANATOMY
OF A
GALAXY

GALAXIES ARE COMPLICATED THINGS, EACH MADE OF
MANY INDIVIDUAL CELESTIAL OBJECTS. THESE INCLUDE
CLOUDS OF GAS AS WELL AS STARS OF VARIOUS TYPES,
MANY OF WHICH MAY HAVE PLANETARY SYSTEMS.
ASTRONOMERS EXPECT THAT EACH GALAXY ALSO
CONTAINS A GIANT BLACK HOLE AT ITS CENTRE, AND
IS EMBEDDED WITHIN A VAST HAZE OF MYSTERIOUS
DARK MATTER.

Anatomy of a galaxy

All galaxies are bound to each other by gravity alone and rotate slowly around a central point. A galaxy does not rotate as a solid object, however. Each individual object follows its own orbit. For example, in the centre of a galaxy, celestial objects complete an orbit in just a few months or less, whereas in the outskirts, celestial objects take hundreds of millions of years to orbit once. So, over millions of years, a galaxy will gradually change its appearance.

From red dwarfs to blue giants

Stars make up the main visible component of most galaxies and come in an array of sizes and temperatures. Stars are vast nuclear furnaces burning in space. A star's mass determines how fast it burns its nuclear fuel. The largest

actually live the shortest lives. This is because they burn the hottest and, even though they contain more raw materials than smaller stars, they use up their nuclear fuel the fastest.

Astronomers use our nearest star, the Sun, as a comparison when talking about other stars. The smallest stars are called red dwarf stars and contain only one tenth of the Sun's mass. These can live for a few hundred billion years and have surface temperatures of just a few thousand degrees Celsius. At the other end of the scale, blue supergiants can contain over 100 times the mass of the Sun. They live for around 10 million years and have surface temperatures that exceed 35,000 degrees Celsius.

The colour of a star betrays its surface temperature. In between the cool red stars and

the hot blue stars, the Sun burns yellow, with a surface temperature of around 6000 degrees Celsius and a lifetime of about 10 billion years.

The population of stars that it contains shapes every galaxy. In elliptical galaxies, powerful gravitational forces have jumbled the orbits of the stars which swarm around the centre like bees around a honey pot. In spiral galaxies, the outer stellar orbits are confined to a disc. This probably mirrors the way that gas clouds have been pulled into the forming galaxy. The central hub of stars in a spiral galaxy is a messy swarm, similar to that found throughout an elliptical galaxy.

We can use a technique called spectral analysis to deduce the chemical composition of stars. This involves splitting the starlight into a

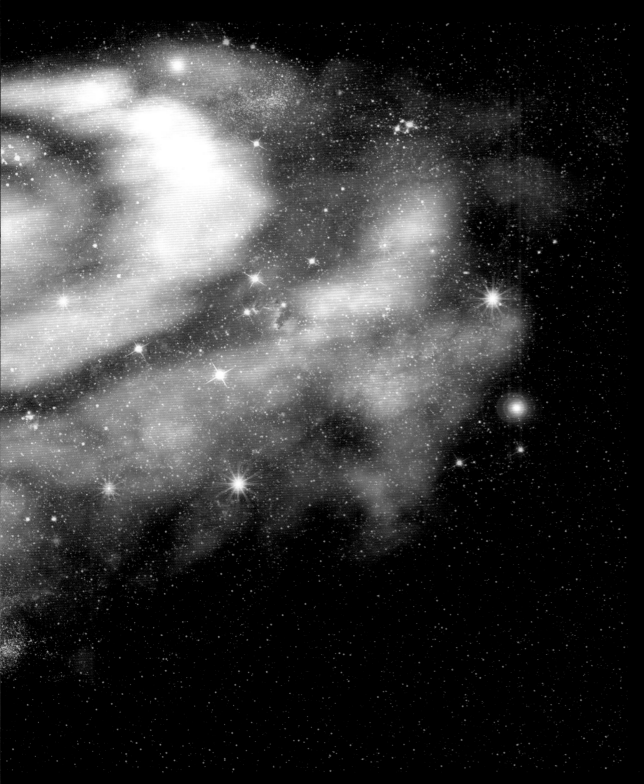

A typical spiral galaxy

The pink light from glowing hydrogen clouds signposts the areas of most recent star formation. These glowing bubbles are blown apart as the stars develop. Star formation takes place on the leading edge of a galaxy's spiral arms.

As the hydrogen bubbles disperse, clusters of new stars are revealed. The blue supergiant stars give the spiral arms their distinctive colour. The leading edge of star formation moves forward, and the newborn stars trail behind, giving the arm its width.

At the trailing edge of the spiral arms, the short-lived blue supergiant stars explode and die while the fainter, yellow and red stars live on. So, underneath the spiral arms is a complete disc of older stars, but they are outshone by the fierce brilliance of their blue cousins.

The centre of the galaxy contains mostly older, long-lived stars. New stars are still formed here, but not with the same frequency as in the spiral arms.

In the very centre of a galaxy lies a supermassive black hole, containing millions or even billions of times the mass of the Sun. These celestial mysteries might be the original seeds around which the galaxy formed.

Some stars are thrown out of the disc of a spiral galaxy. These form a tenuous spherical cloud around the galaxy, called the halo. They are not distributed as densely as in an elliptical galaxy, where a collision between two large galaxies has thrown all the stars around.

rainbow of colours and looking for dark lines within the resulting spectrum. These dark lines are the fingerprints of chemical elements because each type of atom naturally absorbs a different wavelength of light. So, by fingerprinting the stars and other celestial objects in this way, astronomers can gauge the abundance of chemicals not only in the individual objects but also across the universe.

We have discovered that stars are made mostly of hydrogen and helium and that this combination reflects the cosmic abundance of elements across the universe. Together, hydrogen and helium make up 98 percent of all atoms. The remaining 2 percent consists of all the other naturally occurring, heavier chemical elements. These include oxygen, carbon, iron

and uranium to name but a few.

The same abundances are found in the celestial clouds, some of which stretch for hundreds of light years through space. It is within them that new stars form. These clouds contain about one percent of their mass in the form of dust. The dust grains are minuscule, most of them are less than a millionth of a metre across, and they are made predominantly of the heavier chemical elements.

The dust also falls into newborn stars. En route it forms a dark cocoon of matter that hides the forming star from sight. Importantly, inside these cocoons, the dust grains continue to grow. Eventually, planets are produced from this inexorable accumulation of minute seeds.

The appearance of galaxies

As the stellar population ages, a galaxy changes its appearance. As long as the galaxy contains gas from which stars can form, it will continue to shine, not only with older yellow and red stars but also with the blue signature of stellar youth. But as galaxies exhaust their reservoir of gas, star formation will tail off and the blue colour will fade and then disappear.

The distribution of stars changes across a galaxy, although all types are denser towards their centres. Whereas stars in the outskirts of the galaxy are separated quite widely, normally by a few light years, as you approach the centre the separation shrinks to a few light weeks and lower. At the very centre, the density is so great that a giant black hole will probably form.

GALAXIES OF STARS

MILKY WAY

Galaxies are made of stars

The most obvious components of any galaxy are the stars. Each and every one shines like a beacon into space. Every star on this image is a part of our own galaxy, the Milky Way. As countless as they appear, they make up just a tiny fraction of the 100 billion stars our galaxy is believed to contain.

This particular view is towards the centre of our galaxy, which is visible as the orange glow to the upper right. The Earth lies 26,000 light years from the centre, on the trailing edge of a small spiral arm called the Orion spur. To the unaided eye observing the night sky, the light from these stars blurs into a faint band which is why the Milky Way is so-called.

The dark streams in the image are thick lanes of dust that obscure the light of more distant stars. Around these streams the stars tend to look redder. This is because thin veils of dust tend to scatter blue starlight, while leaving the red light virtually untouched. We call this interstellar reddening.

To the bottom left a few pink bubbles of glowing hydrogen gas mark out regions of ongoing star formation.

ANDROMEDA THROUGH DIFFERENT EYES

M31 INFRARED ANDROMEDA

Cool dust

NASA's Spitzer Space Telescope captured this infrared image of the Andromeda Galaxy after 18 hours of continual observation. It shows Andromeda's skeleton of cold dust. Starlight warms this dust but not by much. To show up in this image its temperature cannot be much above minus 220 degrees Celsius.

The image shows a set of small spiral arms twisting away from the galaxy's nucleus. These give way to a prominent ring of dust that matches the ring of star formation in the ultraviolet image.

The image also records the emission of gigantic old stars, glowing with the last feeble rays of infrared light before dying. The infrared radiation from these stars intermingles with that from the cool dust.

M31 ULTRAVIOLET ANDROMEDA

Hot stars

This image of the nearby Andromeda Galaxy was taken with NASA's Galaxy Evolution Explorer (GALEX). The very hottest stars dominate the ultraviolet image. They are the newly formed blue giants whose surfaces radiate at temperatures of tens of thousands of degrees.

Perhaps the most peculiar feature is the bright wide ring of ultraviolet stars 150,000 light years across. No one yet knows what caused this structure to form but it might have been triggered by the gravity of one of Andromeda's nearby satellite galaxies.

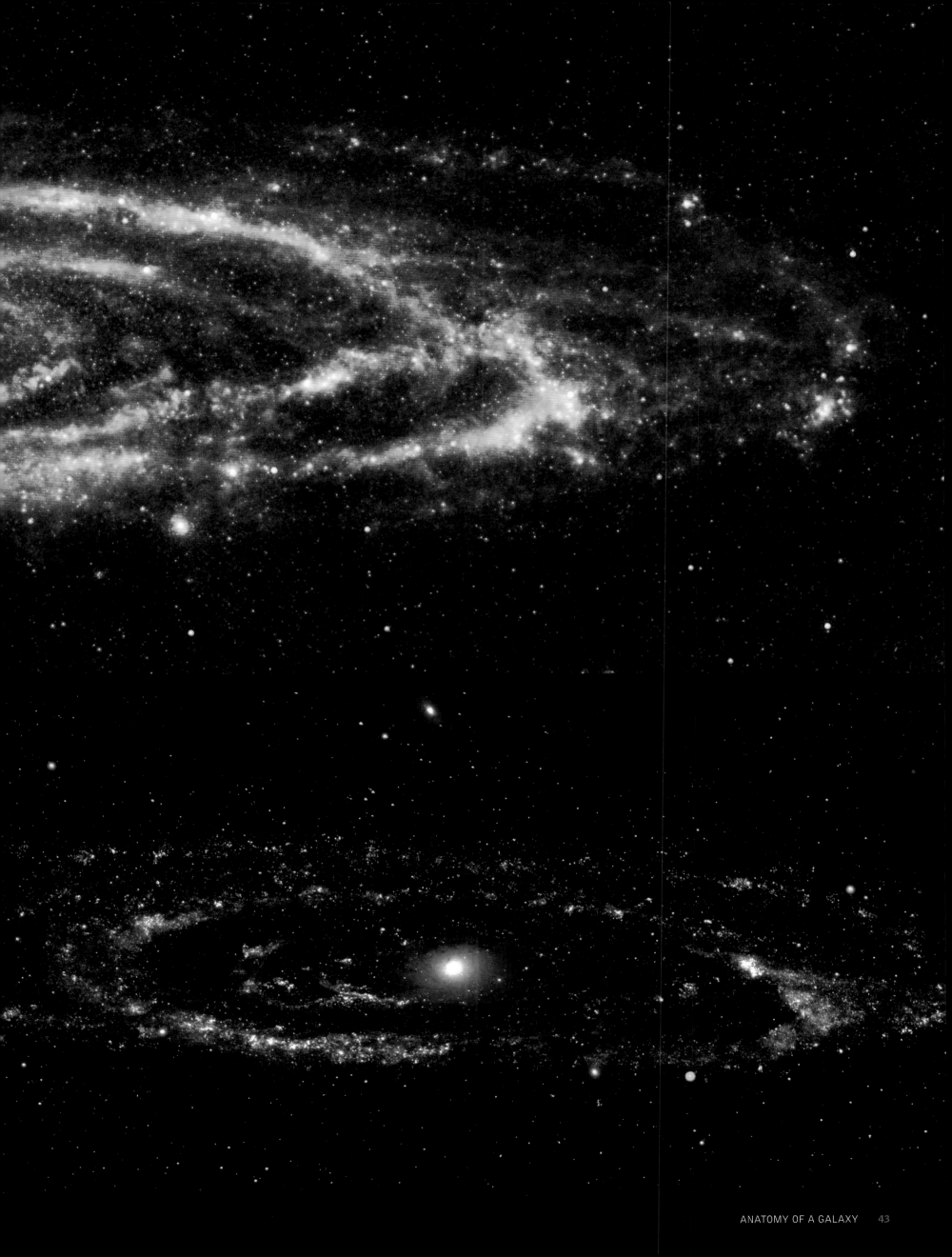

M31 OPTICAL ANDROMEDA

The view by eye
Imagine travelling over two million light years through space. This is what you would see, as you drew close to the Andromeda Galaxy. The light from billions of stars at the centre of the galaxy combines in this image to form a single brilliant mass of light.

STAR-FORMING CLOUDS

NGC 3372 CARINA NEBULA

In the heart of a star-forming cloud

This cloud of gas is a maelstrom of star birth, 50 light years across, with a least a dozen monstrous stars buried inside. Each star contains at least 50 to 100 times the mass of the Sun. Their ultraviolet radiation drives the cloud into a frenzy, sculpting it into the whirling patterns seen here.

The first stars here formed three million years ago, the largest star being Eta Carina. It is now surrounded by a dumbbell-shaped structure thought to be the result of a mighty explosion on its surface. It presages an even larger explosion because Eta Carina is so unstable that astronomers expect it to blow itself to pieces at any time in the next million years. When it does, it will scatter its contents back into the cloud, ready to be incorporated within the next generation of stars.

Star formation is a continual process inside the Carina Nebula. The new stars are born inside dusty pillars of gas. The first sign of a star leaving its cocoon is usually when two jets of luminous gas break out and squirt off in opposite directions, acting as signposts to astronomers, pointing back to where the young star is located.

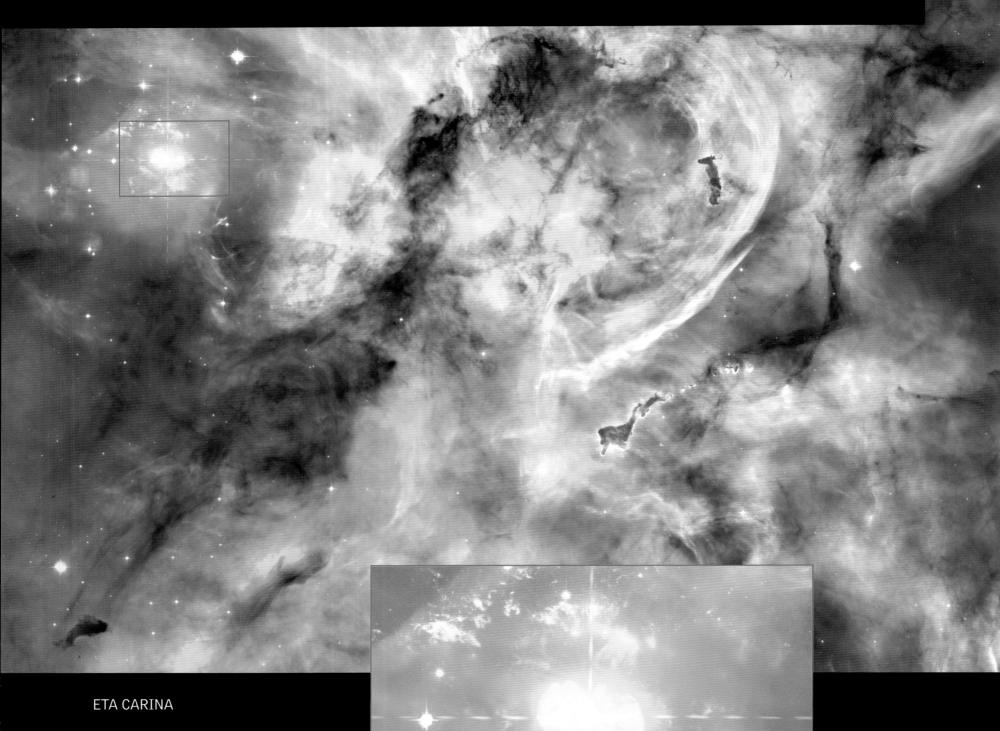

ETA CARINA

Massive star

As stars go, Eta Carina is a heavyweight. It contains more than 100 times the mass of the Sun and, as a result, shines with a furious intensity.

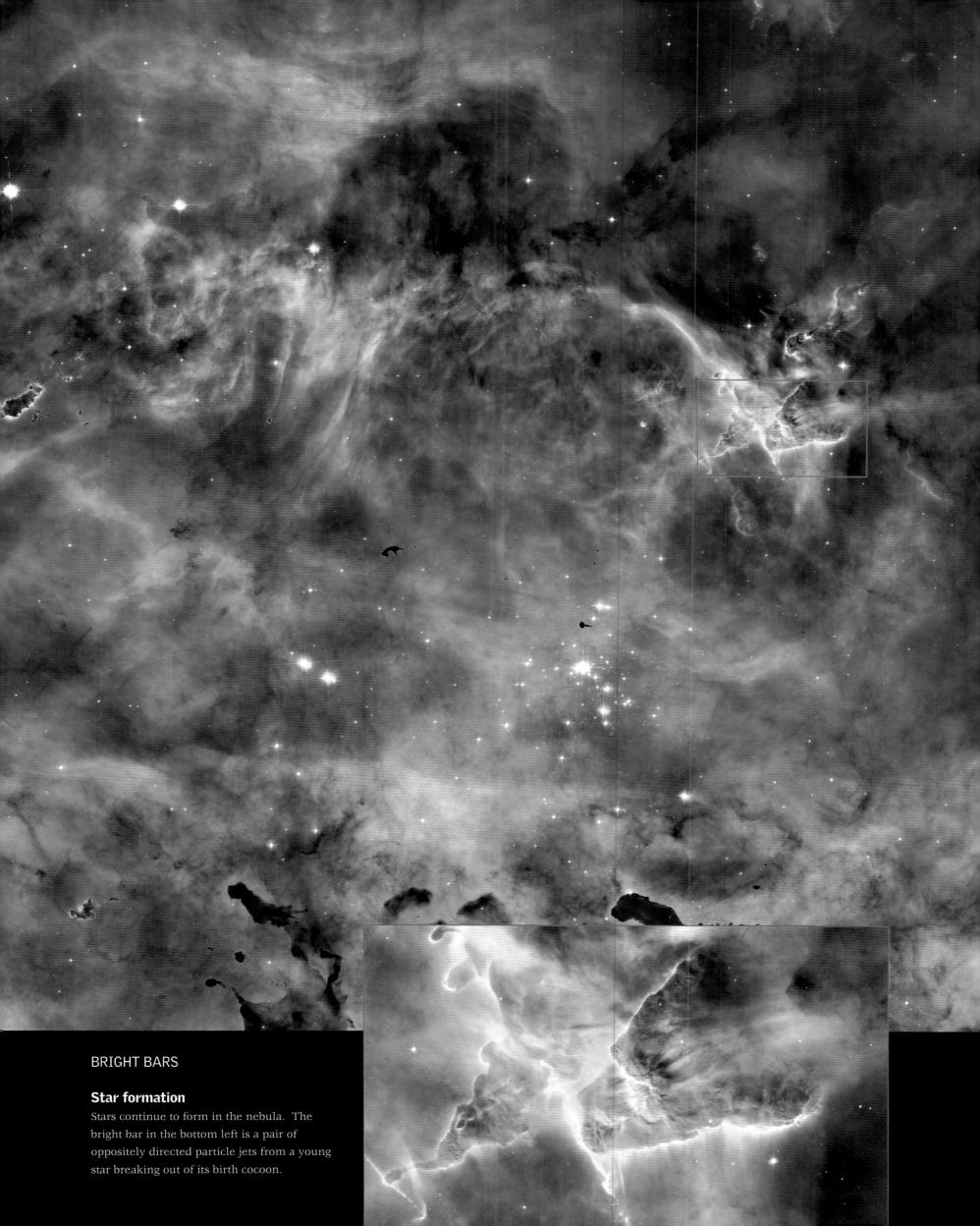

BRIGHT BARS

Star formation

Stars continue to form in the nebula. The
bright bar in the bottom left is a pair of
oppositely directed particle jets from a young
star breaking out of its birth cocoon.

PILLARS OF CREATION

M16 EAGLE NEBULA

Claws of the eagle

The Eagle Nebula spans 20 light years. Hot stars have already formed in this nebula and their ultraviolet light is causing the surrounding gas to glow. These young stars are visible in the upper left portion of the nebula, sitting in front of veils of blue light. Near the centre, vast pillars of dust and dense gas protrude into space.

Astronomers believe that inside these pillars many stars are forming, in a race against time. Can they pull enough gas together to become bona fide stars before the raw material is blown away in the torrent of ultraviolet radiation flooding the nebula? Only time will tell.

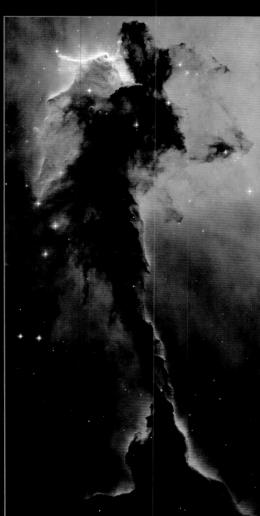

DARK NEBULA

Spire of stars

Stretching for 9.5 light years, if
placed at the base of this dusty
nearest star to us (Alpha Centa
about halfway to the top. This p
others in the Eagle Nebula, is a
new stars.

And like its counterparts, u
from the massive stars in the n
cluster are slowly eroding it aw
are not the same because of the
processing technique that has b
this image. They show differen
elements: blue picks out glowi
red shows the location of hydro

STELLAR NURSERIES

M42 ORION NEBULA

Nearby star factory

The Orion Nebula is the nearest star-forming region to the Earth that has produced massive stars. Located 1500 light years away, it can be seen with the naked eye as a pinkish 'star' in the constellation of Orion. It is the second star in Orion's sword. Through a telescope, four stellar heavyweights that the cluster has produced are revealed, sitting tightly in the centre of the green-yellow glow from oxygen. They are called the Trapezium stars. Their ultraviolet radiation, in particular from the largest star called Theta 1C Orionis, is supplying all of the energy to make this 30-light-year-wide gas cloud glow.

INFRARED ORION NEBULA

Revealing forming stars

By switching the view from optical to infrared wavelengths, most of the glowing gas in the Orion Nebula seems to disappear. In its place, the hundreds of newly formed stars are revealed. These are smaller than those in the Trapezium. Some are similar to our own star, the Sun.

DISSECTING THE ORION NEBULA

What's it made from?

Combining the infrared and optical images
gives further insight. Green swirls reveal
hydrogen and sulphur gas; wisps of red and
orange show polycyclic aromatic hydrocarbons
(PAHs). On Earth, such chemicals appear less
spectacular, being found on burnt toast and in
car fumes. The telescopes also show stars.
Orange-yellow dots are deeply embedded stars,
green ones are those less far in and the blue
dots are stars that lie in front of the nebula.

STELLAR SCULPTORS

NGC 2237 ROSETTE NEBULA

Celestial adornment

Young stars do not just give out light and
ultraviolet radiation. They also blow a stellar
wind of smashed atoms into space. Consisting
mainly of the subatomic particles protons and
electrons, these winds can carve giant cavities
in space that grow around the newborn star like
a giant bubble.

   The Rosette Nebula is a perfect example of
this process. A handful of stars in the centre of
the nebula are producing powerful stellar winds
that push the surrounding nebula away. In the
process, the winds excite the gas and it shines,
as it releases the extra energy into space.

   In effect, the stellar wind is gradually
eroding the nebula and it will eventually
disperse the glowing gas completely. Denser
regions of the nebula show up as dark pillars,
pointing towards the stars in apparent defiance
of their inevitable fate.

N70 EMISSION NEBULA

Celestial chrysanthemum

At 300 light years across, the celestial
chrysanthemum shows what happens when the
nebula has nearly gone. The wispy remains of
gas that surround the young stars mark the
passage of shock waves, set up as the stellar wind
ploughs into denser banks of interstellar gas.

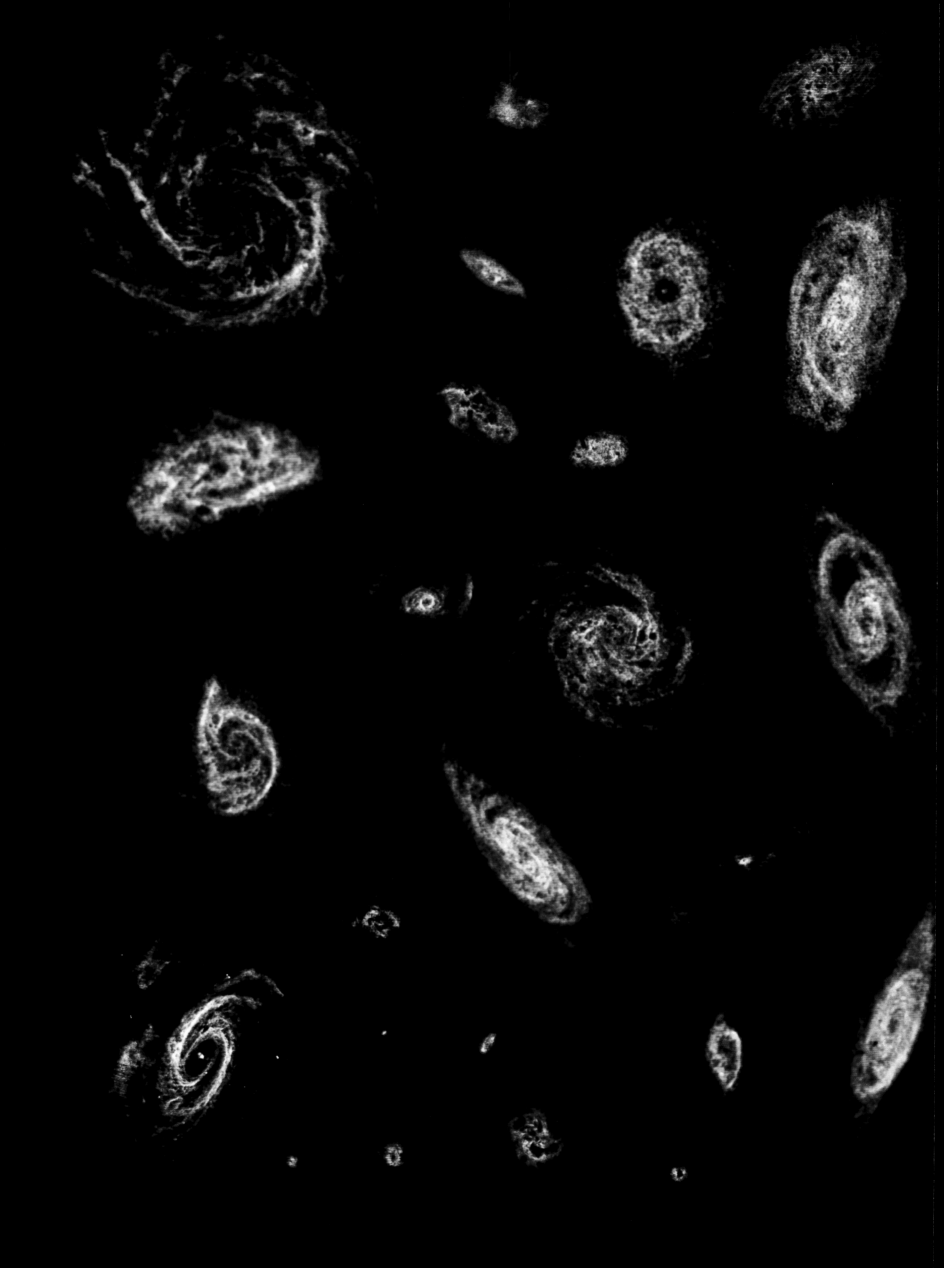

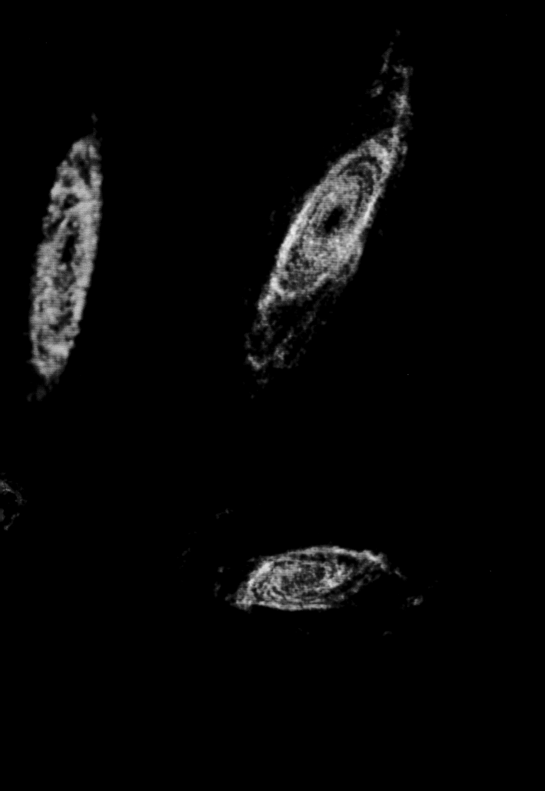

GASSY GALAXIES

NEARBY GALAXY SURVEY

Hydrogen portraits

With a radio telescope, astronomers can completely separate the stars from the gas in a galaxy. Hydrogen atoms do not normally show up in an optical telescope, unless they are sitting close to a massive star and being forced to glow. However, hydrogen appears bright at much longer wavelengths, and so can be seen using radio telescopes.

All the galaxies shown here are visible just from the hydrogen gas. One day this gas might become stars – indeed, some of it may already have been inside stars and has now been returned to space at the end of those stars' lives.

The galaxies are shown on the same scale, revealing their relative sizes to one another. The smallest are dwarf galaxies, found to contain enough raw hydrogen to make approximately 10 million stars like the Sun. At the top end of the scale are the large spiral galaxies, easily identified here because of their complex spiral shapes. These spirals contain enough hydrogen to make 10 billion Sun-like stars. Grand design and flocculent spirals are easily recognisable in these images from the pattern of hydrogen.

Each galaxy then probably contains about ten times more hydrogen, which is currently locked up inside existing stars.

NEWBORN STARS

M45 OPEN CLUSTER

The Seven Sisters

When the large stars have blown away the
surrounding nebula, the rest of the recently
formed stars are revealed. This particular open
cluster of stars is called the Pleiades, or Seven
Sisters. Lying 400 light years away, its name
comes from the tight knot of stars that can be
readily seen by the naked eye.

The term 'open cluster' refers to the fact
that even though the stars are quite close
together, they are not caught up in each other's
gravity and gradually, over time, the cluster
will disperse.

The blue veils that surround the stars are
dust clouds reflecting the starlight. Although,
it is tempting to think that these must be the
remnants of the Pleiades' birth cloud, careful
analysis has shown that it is just a stray cloud
of dust through which the Pleiades are
travelling.

M45 INFRARED PLEIADES

The dusty veils of the Seven Sisters

Infrared wavelengths reveal the full extent of
the dust cloud that the Pleiades are passing
through. The densest portions of the cloud
show up in yellow and red, while the more
diffuse outskirts appear green. The image
also reveals many of the fainter stars that
accompany the Seven Sisters. These include
failed stars called brown dwarfs that did not
accumulate enough gas to start a nuclear fire
in their core.

AE AURIGAE

The Flaming Star

Enormous gravitational forces appear to have
ejected the star AE Aurigae from the Orion Nebula
about 2.7 million years ago. The star itself is a
bright blue youngster, whose energetic ultraviolet
radiation makes nearby gas clouds glow, as the star
speeds past.

To the eye looking through a telescope, the
wisps of gas appear to be tongues of fire, giving it
the nickname 'flaming' star. This image has been
colour coded to show different gases in different
colours. Hydrogen is shown as yellow, oxygen as
violet, and sulphur as blue.

DYING STARS

ESO 172-07 BOOMERANG NEBULA

The nuclear furnace raging inside a star cannot last forever. Most stars can burn steadily for tens of billions of years, but then the supply of hydrogen becomes exhausted. At this point in a star's life, cataclysmic changes begin to happen inside.

During these changes, the stellar wind becomes markedly faster and the star begins to expel its outer layers into space. This process reveals the nuclear core, a blazing mass about the size of the Earth with a temperature of 100,000 degrees Celsius. We call this remnant a white dwarf star.

The Boomerang Nebula shows how such a fate transforms the star to a ghostly cloud of gas in space. Astronomers misnamed these clouds 'planetary nebulae' because, through 18th-century telescopes, they bore a faint resemblance to the newly discovered planet, Uranus.

Nowadays, astronomers think that planets orbiting the dying star might help construct the exotic shapes of many planetary nebulae. So perhaps the name was not such a mistake after all.

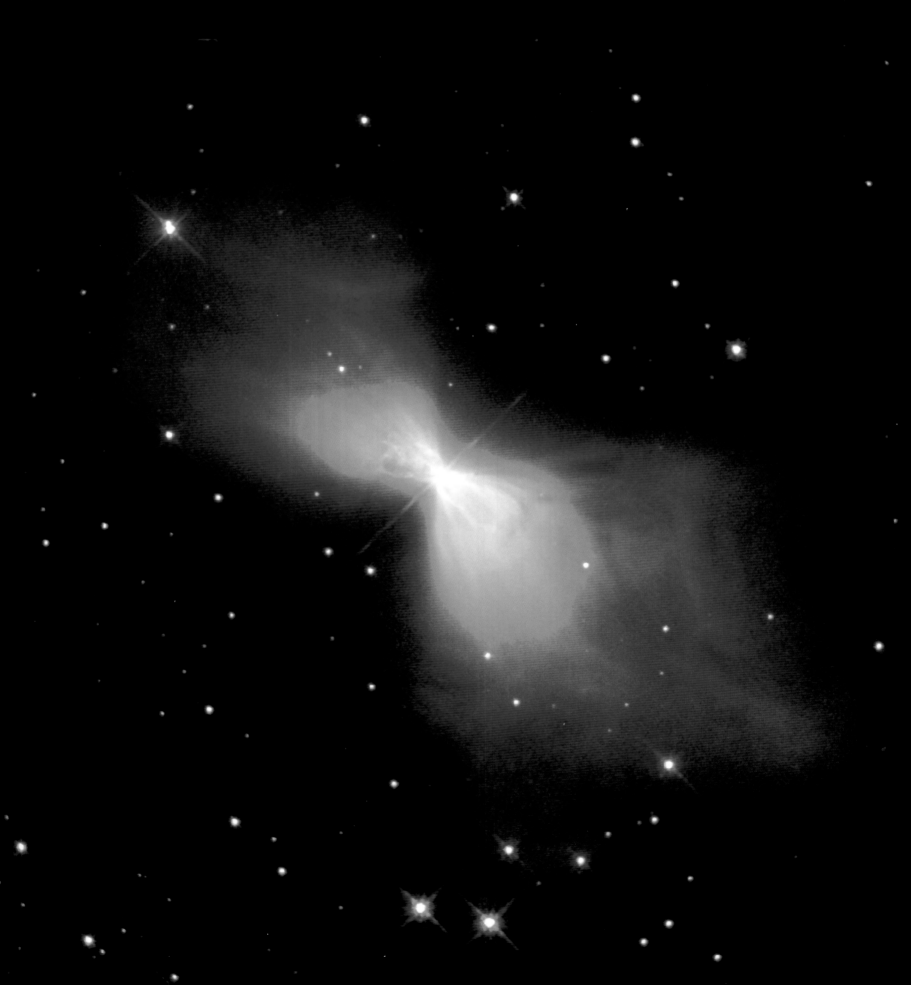

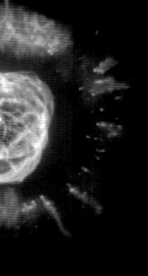

netary
th.

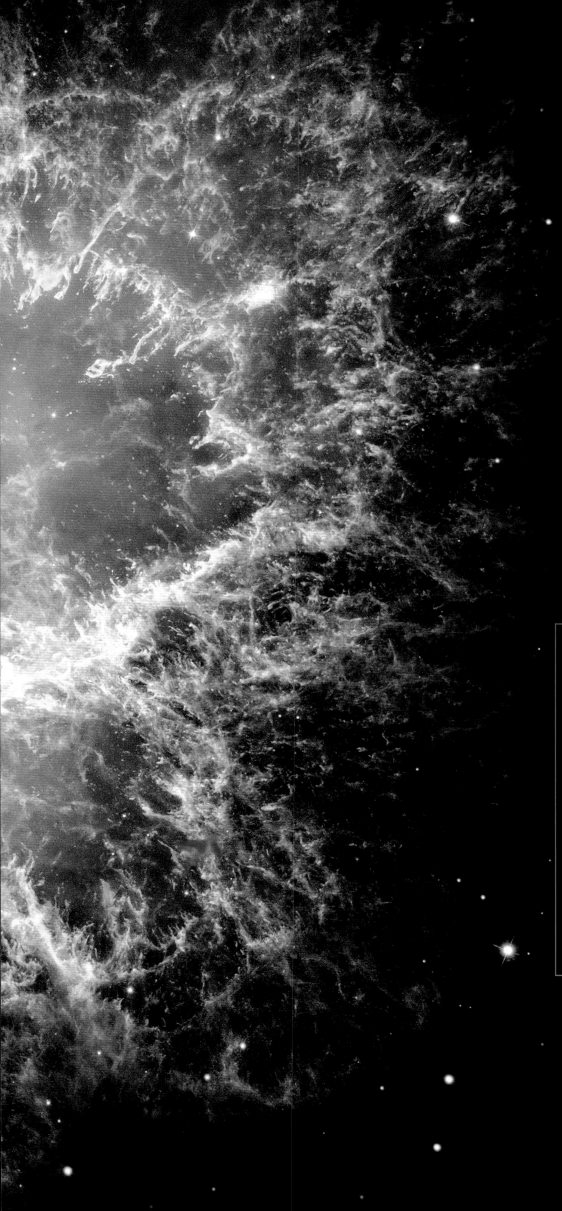

EXPLODING STARS

M1 CRAB NEBULA

Death of a giant

Stars that contain more than eight times the mass of the Sun suffer an even more spectacular fate than becoming a planetary nebula with a white dwarf star. They literally blow themselves to pieces. The fusion reactions inside a giant star produce increasingly heavier chemical elements. When it starts to produce iron, this settles like ash in a fire at the heart of the star. After just a day of furious nuclear reactions, the amount of iron produced in a massive star exceeds the mass of the Sun by half as much again.

Iron cannot be easily fused into anything else, so instead it collapses under the weight of its own gravity to become a compact ball of matter just 15 km (9 miles) across. This is like knocking the foundation out from under a building. The surrounding layers of the star fall inwards where they collide, releasing so much energy that the direction of motion is reversed, and everything apart from the central dense core is exploded away into space.

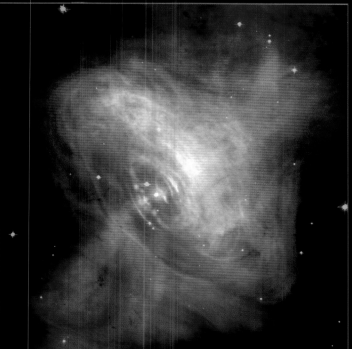

M1 CRAB PULSAR

Heart of the crab

The Crab Nebula is what remains of a star that exploded. The light from this explosion reached Earth in AD 1054. The central remains form a neutron star. It is surrounded by a whirling cloud of gas and continues to emit more than 750,000 times the Sun's energy output, causing the rest of the nebula to glow.

STELLAR SEEDS

NGC 6960

Veil Nebula

Exploding stars perform two functions in a galaxy. The first is to seed it with heavy elements that can then be incorporated into the next generation of stars. The second is to send a shock wave rippling through space in all directions. This wave compresses interstellar gas clouds and can cause them to begin fragmenting into new stars. In this way, dying stars trigger the process of stellar life all over again.

The Veil Nebula lies 2600 light years away and is just part of the 80-light-year wide Cygnus loop. This cosmic bubble of gas is all that remains of the shock wave set in motion by an exploding star 15,000 years ago. As it passes, the shock wave heats gas to 50,000 degrees Celsius, causing it to glow.

Seventeenth-century cataclysm

This is the shock wave from a star that exploded
in 1604. It lies 13,000 light years away yet
astronomer Johannes Kepler witnessed the
brilliant burst of light with his naked eye.
During the intervening four centuries, the
shock wave has grown to a radius of 14 light
years. It continues to expand at 6 million kph
(4 million mph).

THE CENTRE
OF A GALAXY

THE MILKY WAY PANORAMA

Cauldron of stars

The centre of a galaxy is the dense hub around which all of its other stars and nebulae revolve. This is the centre of our own Milky Way as seen at infrared wavelengths. What appears to optical telescopes as an impenetrable sea of dust, is revealed as a complex mass of old stars and dark cocoons holding new stars.

This image spans a few hundred light years across yet captures hundreds of thousands of stars.

In this cauldron of stars, each individual celestial object completes its journey around the centre of the galaxy in just a few decades. Yet at the Sun's location, 26,000 light years from the centre, the orbital period is 230 million years.

BLACK HEART OF THE GALAXY

THE MILKY WAY PANORAMA

Starry sweep

This panoramic view shows the majestic sweep of our galaxy. Half a billion stars are marked on this image, as well as the prominent dust clouds. As many as this sounds, it is only about half a percent of the total number of stars that populate the Milky Way. Astronomers will never see some of these stars, because they cannot peer around the back of the Galaxy to see what lies beyond its centre. They believe they will be very similar, however, to the stars on our side.

SAGITTARIUS A*

Galactic X-rays

Changing the view to X-rays allows astronomers to peer a bit closer to the centre of the Milky Way. This view zooms in on the centre of the Galaxy and reveals a bright patch of X-rays just off to the left. We believe that in this region of space lurks a supermassive black hole that marks the very centre of the Milky Way. It seems likely that most, if not all, galaxies, will have a similar black hole.

RADIO VIEW OF THE CENTRE

Spiralling electrons

This is the closest astronomers have got to capturing an image of the very centre of our galaxy. It was taken with a radio telescope and reveals the radio waves given out by electrons as they spiral around the strong magnetic fields present in the centre of the Milky Way. The brightest blob in the image is thought to be the location of the central black hole. Although it appears tiny in this image, it has swallowed enough matter to make three million stars like the Sun.

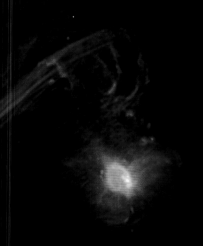

THE ORDER OF THE UNIVERSE

WHEN ASTRONOMERS LOOK INTO THE NIGHT SKY, THEY SEE THE RICH TAPESTRY OF GALAXIES INTERMIXED WITH OTHER CELESTIAL OBJECTS BUT THERE IS NO SENSE OF DISTANCE AT ALL. AS A RESULT, EVERYTHING APPEARS TO SIT ON THE SAME BLANK CANVAS. IN THE PAST, THIS INABILITY TO TELL HOW FAR AWAY OBJECTS ARE HAS CAUSED CONFUSION.

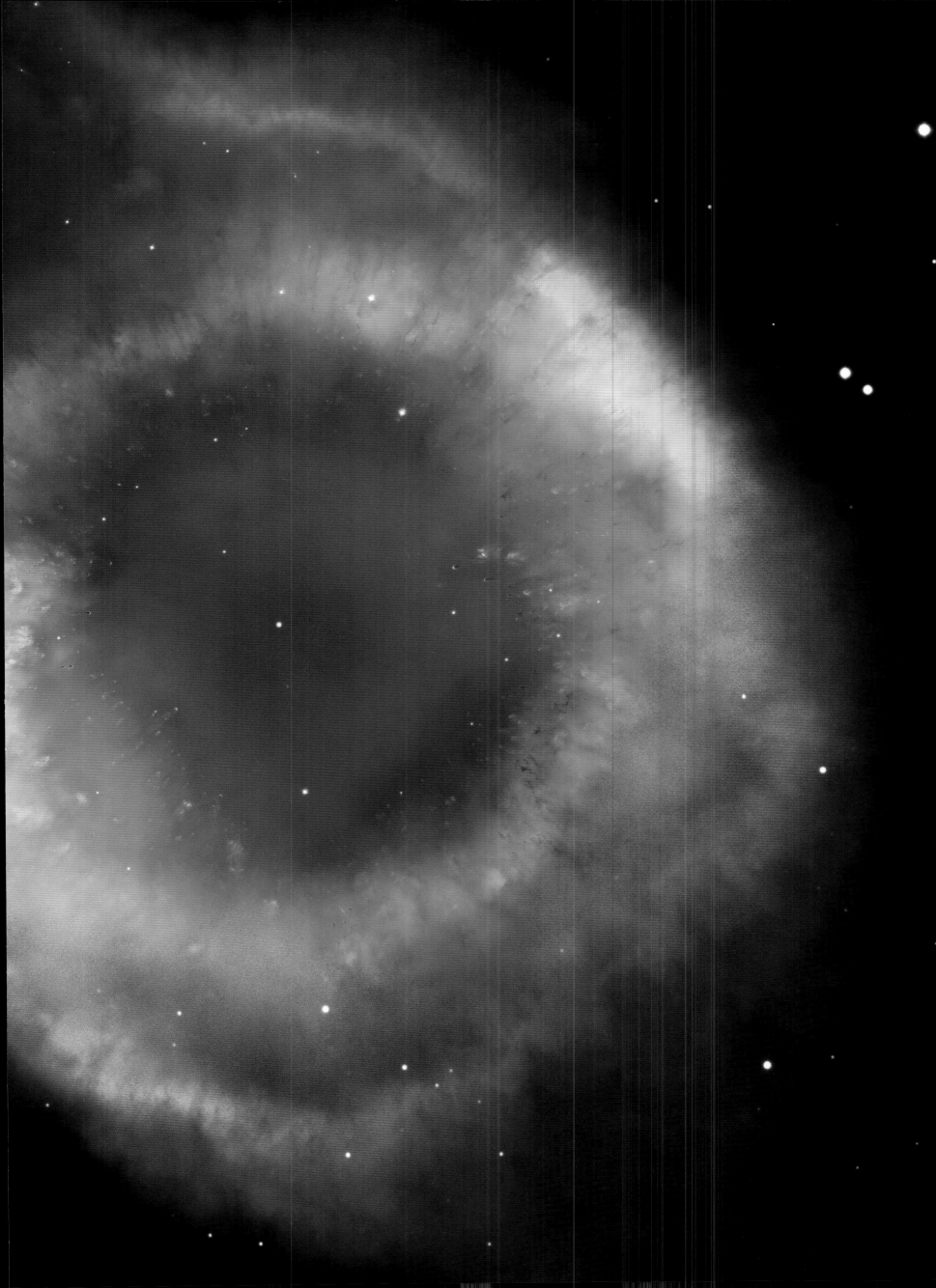

The order of the universe

Initially astronomers believed that the stars in the night sky represented the entire universe. When the telescopes of the late 18th and early 19th century began to show swirling clouds – the so-called nebulae – astronomers first assumed that these were gaseous objects at the same distances as the stars. A particular subset of the nebulae caught their attention. They called them the spiral nebulae because of their enchanting swirling shapes, and they wondered whether these were stars in the process of formation.

Island universes

A number of other astronomers held a different view. They thought that the spiral nebulae were whole collections of other stars. They just appeared small and diffuse because they were so far away and the light from their individual stars merged into one glowing mass. They called this idea the island universe hypothesis because, if they were right, these nebulae were distant collections of stars, every bit as mighty as the Milky Way galaxy where our own solar system resides.

The great American astronomer Edwin Hubble ended the confusion on 1 January 1925. Hubble had used the recently completed 100-inch Hooker Telescope at the Mount Wilson Observatory, in California, to identify individual stars in these 'spiral nebulae'. Most excitingly, some of these stars were Cepheid variable stars.

The brightness of this particular class of stars rises and falls following a regular pattern. In 1908, American astronomer Henrietta Swan Leavitt had measured hundreds of these stars, discovering that the time each one took to pulsate betrayed its absolute brightness.

For example, a Cepheid that completes its variations in just three days is 800 times brighter than the Sun. On the other hand, one with a thirty-day period is 10,000 times brighter than the Sun. Astronomers realized at once that they could use this fact to calculate distances across the heavens.

If any Cepheid variable were found and its period measured, it would be possible to work out how much energy it was pumping out into space and so calculate how bright it would appear if it were close to the Earth. We could then measure its average brightness as seen from Earth, compare this with its calculated brightness and work out how far away it must be. This is because the further away an object, the dimmer it will appear, just as a set of headlights appears fainter the further away the vehicle on the road.

When Hubble identified Cepheid variable stars in the nearby irregular galaxy, NGC 6822, he calculated their distance and proved that it was far beyond the stars of the Milky Way. Modern estimates place the galaxy at 1.8 million light years. Hubble then went on to find Cepheid variables in M33 and M31, proving that they were spiral galaxies in their own right, not just clouds within the Milky Way.

It was a profound discovery. The idea that some of these faint smudges were whole galaxies containing hundreds of billions of stars was a revelation because it showed that the universe was much larger than we had previously imagined.

Standard candles

Astronomers realized that they needed to find other ways of 'unpacking' the montage of the night sky by determining the distances to all the celestial objects. To do that they needed as many ways to estimate distance as possible because, as good as the Cepheid variable technique is, it will work only for nearby galaxies; as we look further out, individual stars cannot be distinguished.

Many other celestial objects are used as 'standard candles' – the term employed for when we know the absolute brightness of an astronomical feature, making it useful for measuring distances across the cosmos. These include the planetary nebulae found within galaxies, as these are bigger and brighter than individual stars. We also use the brief but brilliant flashes of light that represent the death of stars in spectacular explosions. Such supernovae can be seen across a large part of the visible universe, making them a particularly powerful distance indicator.

Today, astronomers have used a number of standard candles to construct what they call the cosmological distance ladder. The ladder is constantly being revised and updated because changes made to the nearby distance scales have a knock-on effect throughout it.

Using the cosmological distance ladder, astronomers estimate the radius of the observable universe to be about 13 billion light years.

Cepheid variables

Parallax

| 1 | 10 | 100 | 1000 | 10^4 | 10^5 |

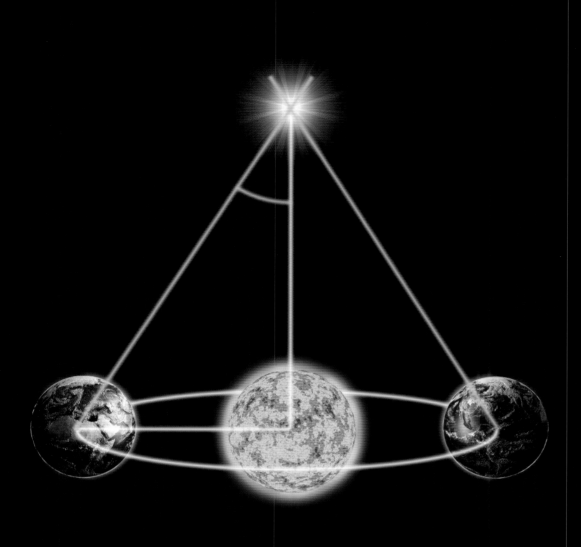

The cosmological distance ladder

The cosmological distance ladder consists of a number of techniques that astronomers can use to gauge distances throughout the universe (see below). They rely on objects of known brightness, such as Cepheid variable stars, planetary nebulae and supernovae of a particular type. It is also possible to judge distance from the rotation of spiral galaxies, using the Tully-Fisher relation. Parallax is another technique employed. This is a highly accurate method of measuring distances but is limited in how far away it can be used.

Parallax works because, as the Earth moves through its orbit, the positions of the nearby stars will change relative to the further stars (see left). It is like holding a finger in front of your face and closing one eye. Note the position of your finger against the objects behind it, and then change the eye you are looking through. Your finger appears to move.

Every six months, the Earth is on the opposite side of its orbit and nearby stars will appear to have moved slightly against the background of further stars. By measuring the angle they appear to move through, astronomers can calculate the distance of the star by basic trigonometry.

The angles we have to measure are so small, however – about 2000th the width of the full moon for the nearest star to the Sun – that parallax can only be used within a restricted area of our own galaxy.

Type Ia supernovae

Tully-Fisher relation

Planetary nebulae

Distance that can be measured, in light years

10^6 10^7 10^8 10^9 10^{10}

BEYOND THE STARS

Unpacking the night sky

Without sophisticated analysis, it is virtually impossible to tell that the galaxies in this image are millions of times further away than the stars. The galaxies themselves are the 'fuzzy' stars. Many of them are ellipticals but there are also a number of spirals and barred spirals visible in the image too. Each one of them contains hundreds of billions of stars.

This collection of galaxies is known as the Norma Cluster. During the 1980s, astronomers realized that the Norma Cluster lies in a region of space that appears to contain an enormously large number of galaxies. So many, in fact, that even though they are over 250 million light years away, the collection's combined gravitational pull is dragging our own galaxy, and those near to us, in its direction.

We call the structure the 'Great Attractor' but our attempts to study it are hampered because it lies almost directly behind the great mass of stars in the centre of our galaxy. The sheer number of stars in this image – all of them in the Milky Way – attests to how difficult it is to see the galaxies of the Norma Cluster.

Confusing comets

Through 18th-century telescopes, individual observations of comets appeared to resemble nebulae and galaxies. It was only the changes in an object's location over several nights that revealed its true identity. The nebulae and galaxies are part of the background of the fixed stars and appeared not to move.

M102

A duplicate entry?

There are 110 objects on the Messier list, although number 102 is disputed. Some observers think that this entry is a duplicate of M101, the Pinwheel Galaxy; others believe it is this galaxy, an edge-on lenticular galaxy known as NGC 5866.

CATALOGUING THE DISTANT UNIVERSE

M81

The Messier Catalogue

During the 18th century, astronomers were interested in the fleeting appearance of comets in our solar system. Charles Messier kept and consulted a catalogue of nebulae and galaxies solely to prevent him from thinking he had discovered new comets, when he had simply stumbled across a known nebula. He actually called the nebulae the 'vermin' of the skies. Nowadays galaxies and nebulae have become objects of fascination that we want to observe, but we still refer to the Messier catalogue for their labels; it is the principal list of bright galaxies and nebulae.

NGC 2442

The New General Catalogue

William Herschel and his son John Herschel continued the work of Charles Messier during the latter years of the 18th century and the beginning of the 19th. William catalogued the northern hemisphere, and John, the southern. The list was completed and finally published in the 1880s by Johan Ludvig Emil Dreyer, a Danish astronomer who worked in Irish observatories. It contains nearly 8000 objects and was called the New General Catalogue. The NGC objects are generally a little fainter than the Messier objects, so were harder to find. Dreyer also compiled two more catalogues of 5000 further objects, known today as the Index Catalogue.

THE OUTSKIRTS OF A GALAXY

Globular cluster

The globular clusters swarm around the Milky Way in the spherical region of space that surrounds our galaxy and is known as the halo. Globular clusters are old objects whose origin is thought to date from the formation of the galaxy. Each contains between 100,000 and 10 million stars and is more or less spherical because the stars in them orbit at many different angles.

We see globular clusters around many other galaxies, so believe that they are a ubiquitous feature of galaxy formation. Perhaps they come together as the galaxy itself is forming or maybe some of them are 'debris' created and thrown out when galaxies collide.

This particular globular cluster is M80. It belongs to the Milky Way, is located 28,000 light years away from Earth and contains over 100,000 stars.

Omega Centauri

Fifty thousand stars are packed into this image
(right) that shows just the core of the Omega
Centauri globular cluster. The area spans a
distance of 13 light years. An image showing
the same area of space, but in our section of the
Milky Way, would hold just six stars. The whole
cluster can be seen in the image below. Omega
Centauri is such a large globular cluster,
containing 10 million stars, that astronomers
wonder if it is all that remains of a galaxy that
was swallowed by the Milky Way.

JUST BEYOND
THE GALAXY

NGC 292 SMALL MAGELLANIC CLOUD

A satellite galaxy

Beyond the realm of the globular clusters of the
Milky Way, lie the Large and the Small
Magellanic Clouds. They are only visible from
the southern hemisphere and are named after
Portuguese explorer Fernando de Magellan,
who brought them to Europe's attention in
1519, after his historic voyage around the world.

The Small Magellanic Cloud is located about
210,000 light years away. Together with its
bigger brother, it has been traditionally called a
satellite galaxy of the Milky Way. Recently,
however, astronomers have begun to wonder
whether it is just passing by our galaxy rather
than in orbit around it.

The Small Magellanic Cloud is only one-
tenth of the size of the Milky Way, at just 10,000
light years in diameter. It contains several
hundred million stars. Although it is now an
irregular galaxy, it may once have been a dwarf
barred spiral that has been pulled out of shape
by the Milky Way's gravity. In return, its gravity
and that of the Large Magellanic Cloud is
warping the disc of the Milky Way slightly.

It was while observing the Small Magellanic
Cloud that Henrietta Swan Leavitt discovered
the period–luminosity relation of Cepheid
variables, which subsequently allowed Edwin
Hubble to measure the distances to other
galaxies.

CEPHEID VARIABLES

The Hubble Space Telescope
Extragalactic Distance Scale Key Project

The Hubble Space Telescope was named after Edwin Hubble because one of the most important jobs the telescope had to perform was to calculate the distances to far-away galaxies, work that the man had begun many decades earlier. Astronomers called it the Hubble Space Telescope Extragalactic Distance Scale Key Project. Over the course of the telescope's first decade in space, the project team observed 18 galaxies out to a distance of 65 million light years. They discovered almost 800 Cepheid variable stars, allowing them to determine the distance to these galaxies more accurately than ever before.

Before Hubble was launched, astronomers had disagreed about how to gauge distances in the universe precisely, once we looked beyond those galaxies in which individual Cepheid variables could be observed. As a result some distance estimates were twice as large as others. Because the telescope discovered Cepheids in more distant galaxies, the calculations could be revised. They showed that the correct distance was roughly halfway between the previous estimates – the perfect compromise.

NGC 4603

Searching for Cepheids

When calculating intergalactic distances, astronomers typically have to work from an image like this. Buried in this star field of NGC 4603 are four precious Cepheid variable stars. The project team hunted them down, in order to monitor their steady pulsation and so gauge the distance to this galaxy – 108 million light years.

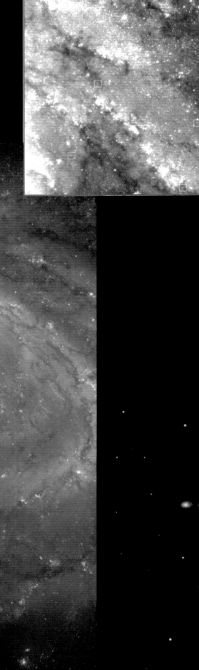

PLANETARY NEBULAE

Large bright measuring rings

Planetary nebulae can also be used as standard candles to gauge distances. Because they are large bubbles of glowing gas, up to a few light years across, they can be seen at even greater distances than Cepheid variable stars. To find them we look for the tell-tale signs of oxygen gas that give away the planetary nebulae, and then measure the brightness of as many as we can find. These are plotted on a diagram that shows the number of planetary nebulae at each brightness value. When comparing this curve with a similar one for planetary nebulae in our Milky Way, we can estimate the distance of the other galaxy.

IC 4406 RETINA NEBULA

Marbled planetary nebulae

As a planetary nebula expands into space it sometimes runs into other clouds of matter. The criss-cross of dark lanes producing the marbling effect on this planetary nebula (below) is caused by a lattice of dusty matter that the expanding cloud of gas is about to engulf. The dark lanes contain matter 1000 times denser than the glowing gas.

M27 DUMBBELL NEBULA

Mature planetary nebulae

As the first planetary nebula discovered, the Dumbbell (below) intrigued eighteenth-century astronomers. Situated 1200 light years away, this giant bubble of gas glows with the equivalent light of 100 Suns. At its centre, the star that the gas originally belonged to still shines with a surface temperature of 85,000 degrees Celsius.

HEN

You

This
loca
take
not
disp
cosm
is ab
time

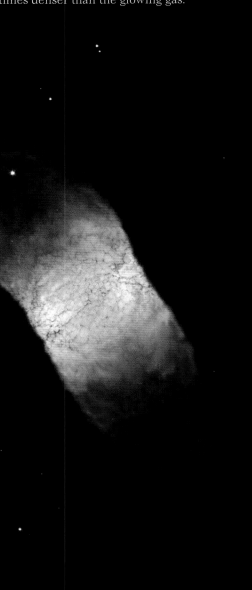

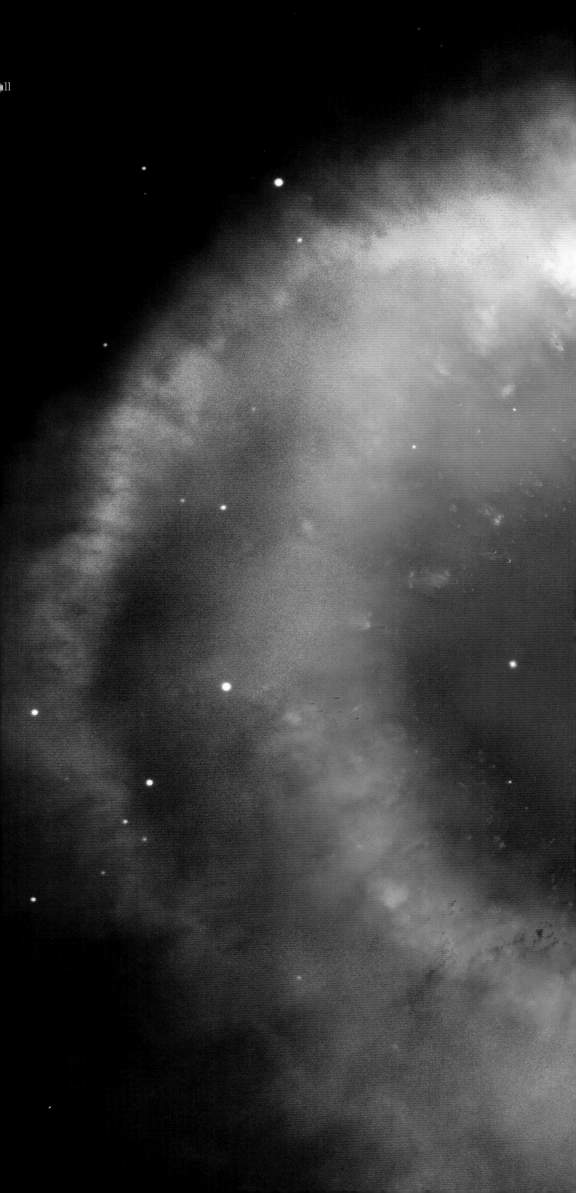

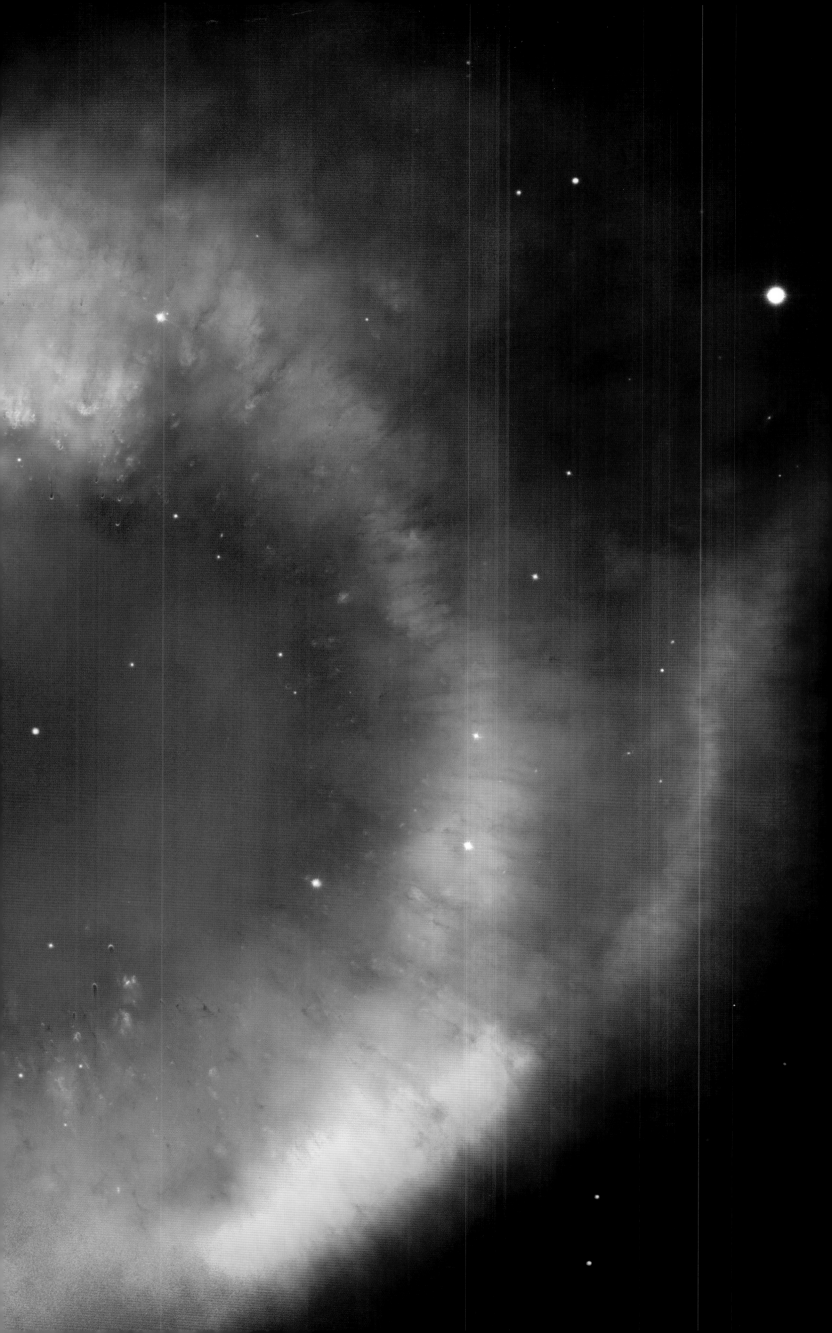

SPINNING
SPIRALS

NGC 1309

The Tully–Fisher relationship
During the 1970s and 1980s, astronomers
R. Brent Tully and J. Richard Fisher noticed
that the speed with which a spiral galaxy spins
is related to its brightness. This means that,
by measuring a galaxy's rate of rotation, we
can use the entire galaxy as a standard candle
and calculate its distance.

Why should this be the case? The speed at
which a galaxy rotates is driven by gravity and
so must be related to the amount of matter it
contains. Similarly, the amount of atoms in a
galaxy must have a bearing on how many stars
it can form, and so its luminosity must also be
dependent on its mass.

NGC 1309 is a spiral galaxy 100 million light
years away.

NGC 3370 SILVERADO GALAXY

Swirling spectra
We can calculate the rotation speed of a galaxy
by isolating the spectral fingerprints that
appear in its light and by measuring the width
of these features. The faster a galaxy is rotating,
the wider these spectral lines will be. The
easiest galaxies to take these measurements for
are the edge-on spirals.

NGC 3370, the Silverado Galaxy, is 98
million light years away.

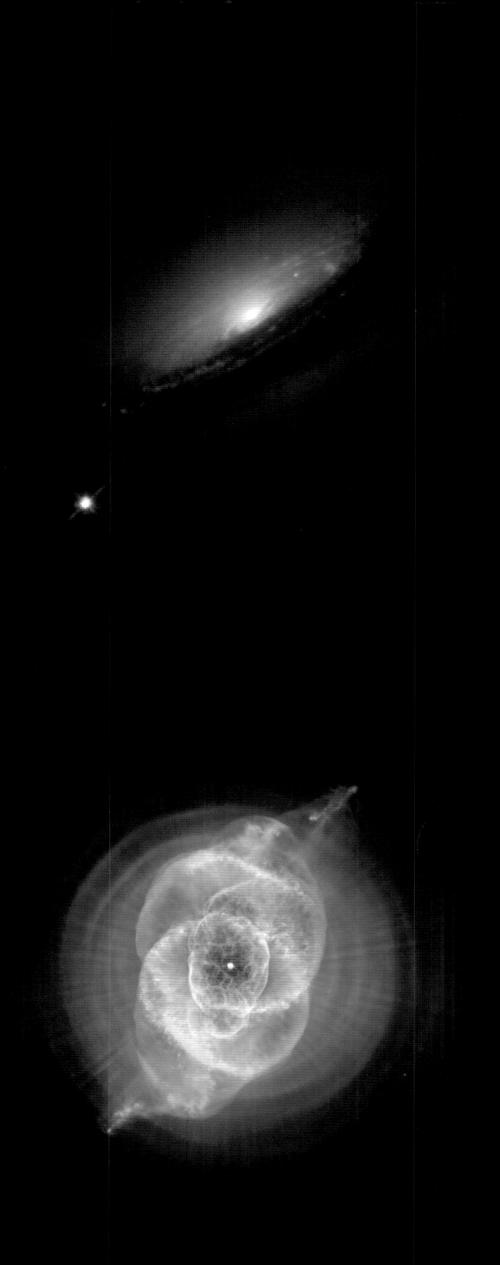

SUPERNOVAE AS SIGNPOSTS

SN 1994D

Exploding milestones

When a massive star explodes as a supernova, it becomes so bright that for a few weeks it outshines all the other stars in its galaxy. If we spot one in time, a supernova can be used as a standard candle for its host galaxy. Supernovae are so bright they can be used for even the most distant galaxies in the universe.

This is the image of a supernova (lower left) that exploded in the very outskirts of the spiral NGC 4526. Its light reached Earth in March 1994 and allowed astronomers to calculate that the galaxy is 108 million light years away.

NGC 6543 CAT'S EYE NEBULA

White dwarf companions

The best kind of supernova for determining distances is one that develops from a white dwarf star caught in orbit around another star. In this situation, the gravity from the white dwarf can pull gas from the surface of its companion star. The gas builds up on the surface of the white dwarf until the mass exceeds a precise limit roughly one and a half times the mass of the Sun. Suddenly, the white dwarf collapses and the ensuing explosion blows it to pieces. These explosions are called type Ia supernovae. They all occur with approximately the same brightness, allowing astronomers to use them as standard candles. The Cat's Eye Nebula holds a white dwarf at its centre, but this particular one is isolated in space and so can never become a type Ia supernova. Many others aren't so lucky.

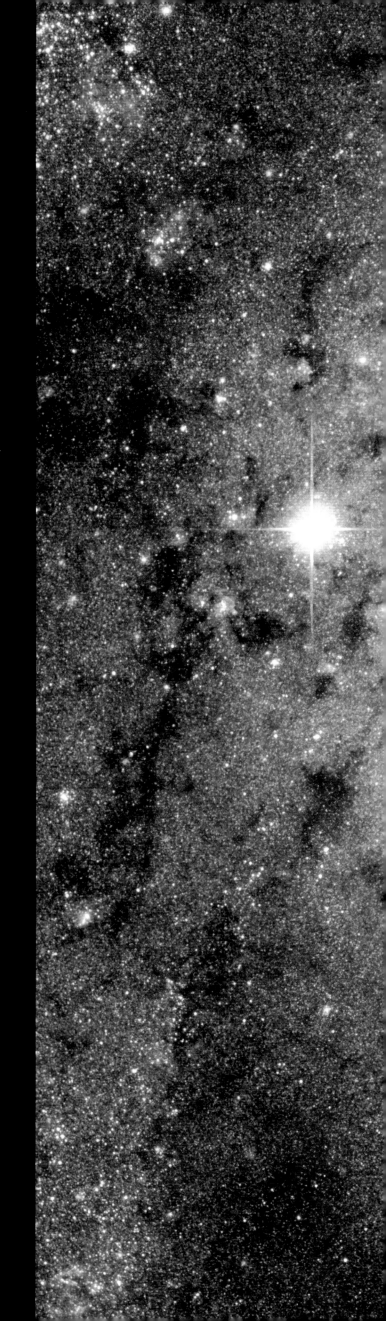

THE EXPANDING UNIVERSE AND THE BIG BANG

WHILE MEASURING THE DISTANCE TO DIFFERENT GALAXIES, EDWIN HUBBLE MADE AN ASTOUNDING DISCOVERY. IT SEEMED THAT MOST GALAXIES WERE MOVING AWAY FROM THE MILKY WAY AND THAT THE FURTHER AWAY A GALAXY WAS, THE FASTER IT WAS RECEDING.

Vesto Slipher, an astronomer at the Lowell Observatory in Arizona, had noticed the first clue to this behaviour back in 1912. Night after night, Slipher had been collecting the light from M104, the Sombrero Galaxy, and splitting it into a spectrum. His intention was to analyze the chemical fingerprints of the galaxy and so deduce its composition. After a total of 40 hours of observation, he looked at the spectrum and saw that something was not quite right. There was a dark line that could only be from the presence of sodium atoms, but it was in the wrong position.

Instead of appearing in the spectrum at the expected wavelength of 589 nanometres (billionths of a metre), the sodium line in M104 was shifted to 591 nanometres. The only thing that could change the wavelength of a spectral line like this is the Doppler effect, indicating that that the object was moving.

In this case the spectral line was stretched, and such a stretch meant that M104 and the Milky Way had to be moving apart. The effect is similar to the way an emergency vehicle's siren changes pitch as it drives past. On approach the siren's sound is squashed, forcing its pitch higher. On retreat, the sound is stretched, lowering the pitch. With light, squashing it makes it more blue while stretching shifts it further towards the red end of the spectrum. When Slipher calculated M104's velocity, he found it was travelling at an incredible 3.9 million kph (2.4 million mph). Slipher's observation of other spiral galaxies showed that most were receding too, all with different speeds.

Receding galaxies

Hubble and his assistant Milton Humason picked up this thread during the late 1920s, in their pioneering work to determine the distances to galaxies. Eventually they showed that the more a galaxy's light was stretched – redshifted as it became known – the further away it was. The realization offered another way to gauge distances in the universe. But astronomers were left with one overwhelming question: what could be causing the galaxies to recede at such a furious pace?

Albert Einstein and his general theory of relativity supplied the answer. The equations that Einstein had deduced to explain gravity made a startling prediction: space itself must be expanding and carrying the galaxies with it.

As astronomers came to terms with the

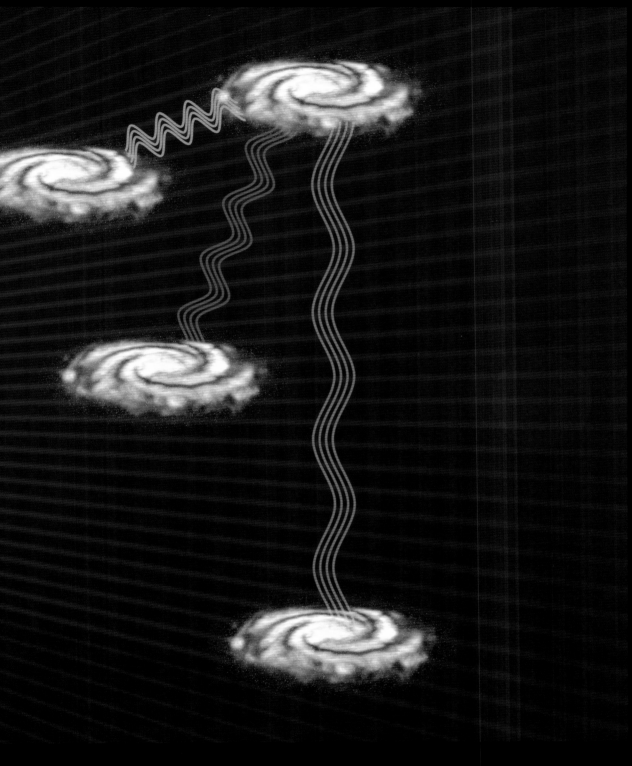

Cosmic cake mixtures

The redshift, as caused by the expansion of the universe, is a great way to calculate distance. This is because the further away a galaxy is, the more its light will be redshifted.

The expanding universe can be understood by thinking of baking a cake. The dough mix is the universe and we can sprinkle in some raisins to represent the galaxies. As the dough rises it carries the embedded raisins with it, forcing them apart from their neighbours. So, the further one raisin is from another, the more dough mix there is in between and the further it will be forced apart.

We talk of redshift as a shorthand way of referring to how much the universe has expanded since a particular galaxy emitted the light we are observing. For example a redshift of one means that the light has been doubled in length. This, in turn, means that when the light from that galaxy was released, the universe was half the size it is today, and therefore roughly half its age.

In other words, if the universe doubles its size it also doubles the wavelength of light travelling through it.

The cosmic microwave background radiation was released into the universe at around a redshift of 1000, meaning that the universe has doubled in size 1000 times since the release of that radiation.

expanding universe, another stunning conclusion hit them. If it was expanding, the universe must have been smaller in the past. But how small?

Birth of the universe

In 1927, the Belgian Catholic priest Georges Lemaître first proposed the hypothesis of the primeval atom, in which he suggested that the entire universe sprang from a single compacted 'atom' at some time in the remote past. The expanding universe as shown by Hubble and Humason was a compelling piece of evidence for this hypothesis.

And so astronomers began to believe that perhaps the universe was once a highly compacted object that suddenly exploded in some sort of 'big bang'. This term was actually coined derisively by the British astronomer Fred Hoyle during a radio broadcast on 28 March 1949, on the BBC. At around this time, the Ukrainian physicist George Gamow used the idea of the big bang to show that it explained the overwhelming quantity of hydrogen and helium that we see today. If the universe began with nothing but the simplest chemical element, hydrogen, Gamow showed that the intense heat of the universe shortly after the big bang took place would have caused a quarter of the hydrogen to fuse into helium, almost the exact proportions that astronomers were deducing from observations.

It was another triumph for the big bang theory but perhaps boldest of all, Gamow made a prediction: radiation from the initial fireball that forged the helium would still linger in the universe today. Because of the expansion of space it would have been stretched into the microwave region of the radio waves, but it should be detectable.

When radio engineers Arno Penzias and Robert Wilson found this microwave background in 1964, using a radio telescope in New Jersey, astronomers realized at once that it was a great triumph. The discovery convinced almost all astronomers that the universe had to have begun in a big bang. For their work, Penzias and Wilson were awarded the 1978 Nobel Prize in physics.

The big bang is now thought to be the beginning of time and space, and of cosmic evolution.

NEARBY GALAXY

M31 ANDROMEDA GALAXY

Collision course

Only on small cosmic scales is gravity powerful enough to overcome the expansion of the universe. The Andromeda Galaxy, M31, is one of the handful of galaxies that is not receding from the Milky Way. This is because, with just 2.5 million light years separating them, the two giant spirals are so close, cosmically speaking, that they are gravitationally bound to one another. In fact, they are conducting a slow pirouette, around a common centre.

Calculations show that as the Milky Way and Andromeda follow their orbits, they are actually on a collision course with one another. Somewhere between 5 billion and 10 billion years in the future, the outskirts of the two galaxies will touch. The night sky will be filled with a second band of misty light, this one from the combined light of the looming Andromeda galaxy.

Although both galaxies will survive this close encounter and move apart again, their beautiful spiral arms are certain to be destroyed by the interplay of gravitational fields. They will become irregular galaxies but remain in the grip of each other due to gravity.

Eventually, the Milky Way and Andromeda will be drawn back together and this time they will merge into a single giant galaxy, probably elliptical.

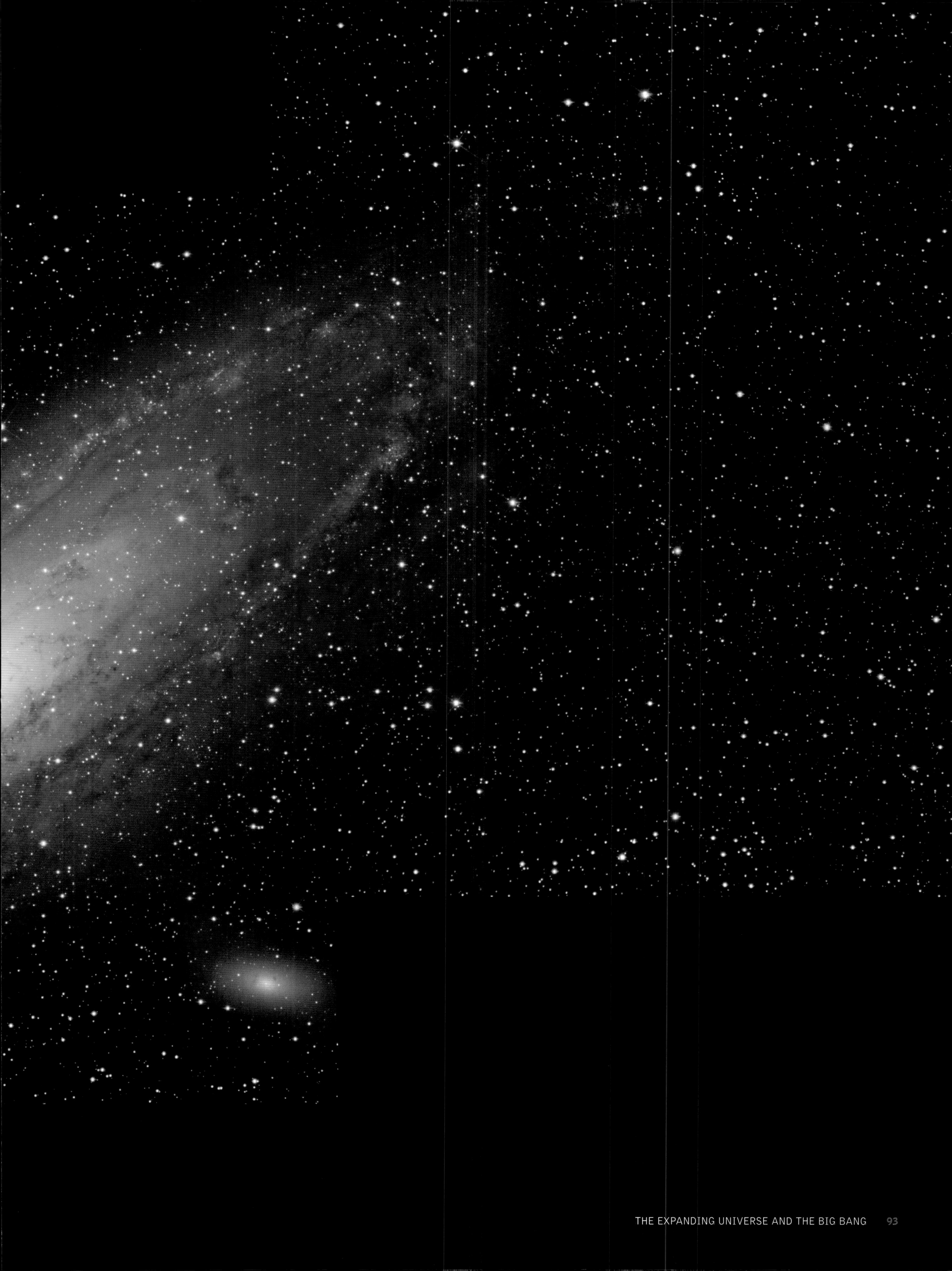

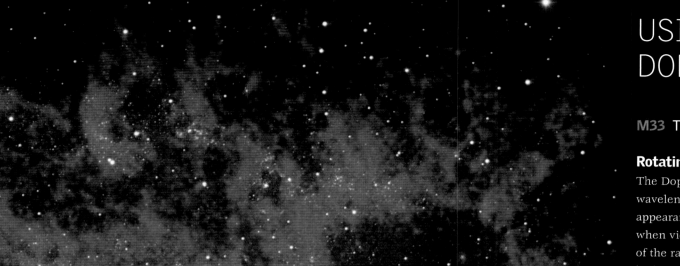

USING THE
DOPPLER SHIFT

M33 TRIANGULUM GALAXY

Rotating spirals

The Doppler effect can work at radio
wavelengths as well as optical ones. This is the
appearance of neighbouring spiral galaxy M33
when viewed at radio wavelengths (below). All
of the radio 'light' shown here is coming from
hydrogen gas, not yet confined inside stars. The
brightness shows how much hydrogen is
present at that location. When this is
superimposed upon an optical image of the
galaxy, there is a surprise for astronomers.

Although in normal light M33 appears to be
only about one-third the size of our own galaxy,
when viewed at radio wavelengths the
hydrogen gas shows that there is more than
meets the eye. By superimposing the radio
image in blue over the optical one (left), the
size of the galaxy is significantly extended.

The hydrogen gas as shown by the radio
telescope can be analyzed for the Doppler shift.
Where the gas is travelling towards the radio
telescope, the radio waves are squashed slightly
(shown in bottom image as bluer colours).
Where the gas is travelling away from the radio
telescope, the radio waves are stretched slightly
(shown in bottom image as redder colours). It
is immediately obvious from the radio waves
that M33 is rotating.

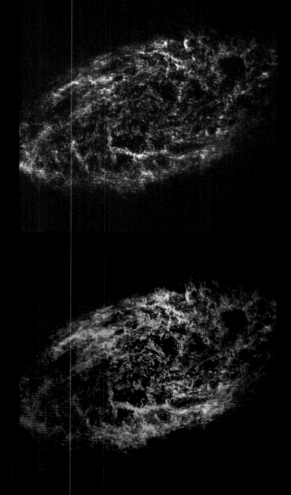

SPACE GROWING BIGGER

The cause of the redshift

Despite its superficial similarity to the Doppler effect, the cosmological redshift arises in a very different way. With the Doppler effect, an object is actually moving. As the early 20th-century cosmologists began calculating galactic recessional velocities, they found themselves astonished by the speeds and wondered what could possibly accelerate a whole galaxy to a speed of millions of kilometres or miles per hour.

Einstein's explanation of an expanding universe provided the answer: the galaxies themselves are not moving through space at these great speeds but the space between the galaxies is expanding, like a piece of stretched rubber. So these are not strictly Doppler shifts. The light from the galaxies is redshifted because it is stretched as the space in which it is travelling expands.

It is like drawing a wavy line on a deflated balloon and then filling it with air. The distance between peaks on the wavy line, the wavelength, is stretched by the inflation of the balloon. So it is with light in the expanding universe.

The galaxies can experience a Doppler shift as well, because of their orbital motion around other galaxies in a cluster of galaxies. This is usually small compared with the cosmological redshift.

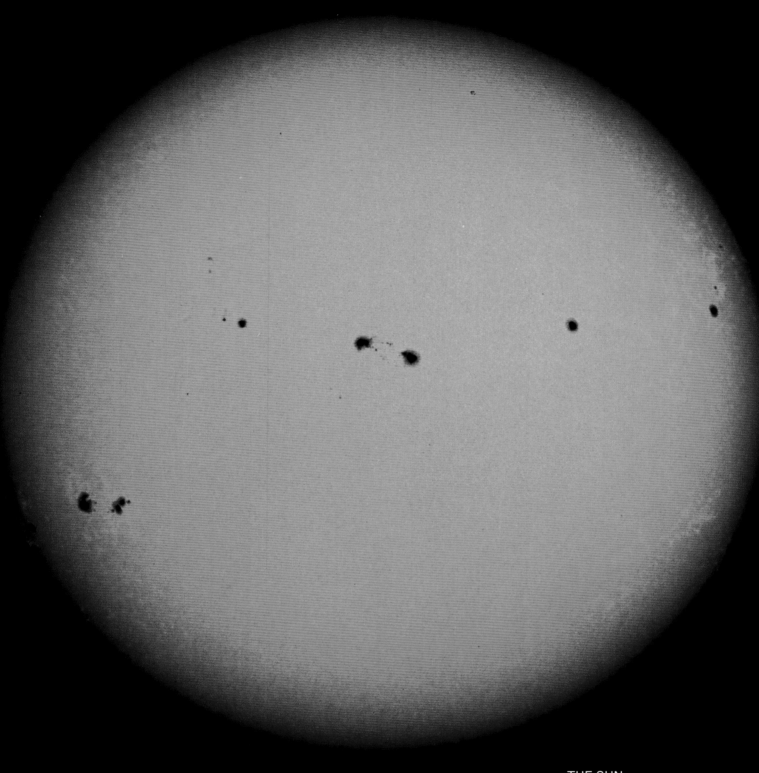

THE SUN
Light travel time: 8 minutes

WINDOWS ON THE PAST

Archaeology of the heavens

On Earth, light appears to travel instantaneously between points. This is an illusion
created by the fact that light travels so fast. In
the wider universe, the distances become so
large that the light travel time can become
significant. It means that we do not see
celestial objects as they appear now, but as they
appeared earlier in the history of the universe.
Astronomers call this an object's look-back time
and it is closely related to an object's distance
in light years. For example, if an object is 1000
light years away, then we see it as it appeared
to be 1000 years ago.

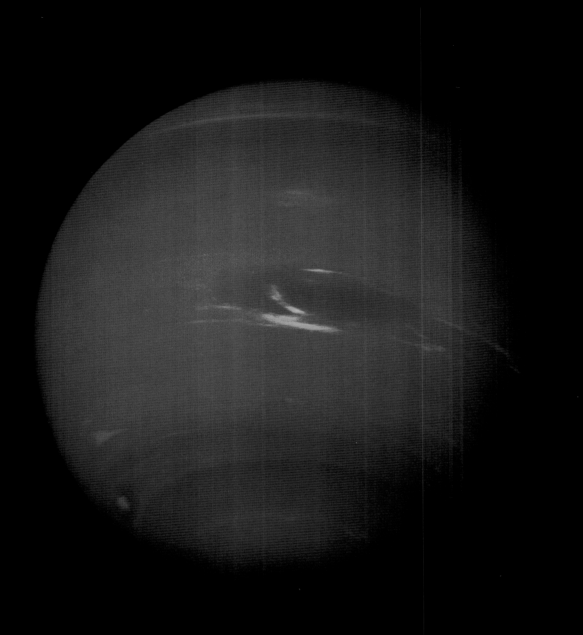

NEPTUNE
Light travel time: 4.16 hours

M52 STAR CLUSTER
Light travel time: 5000 years

M82 NEARBY GALAXY
Light travel time: 12 million years

DISTANT GALAXIES
Light travel time: 12 billion years

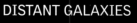

INTO THE
DEEP FIELD

THE DISTANT UNIVERSE

Thousands of galaxies

Some of the farthest objects visible in the
universe can be seen in this image. We call
observations of this type 'deep fields' because
the field of view is deeper into the universe
than ever before. It took the Hubble Space
Telescope nearly 40 hours to capture this
image. It was time well spent because most of
these celestial objects had never been seen
before. Astronomers deliberately targeted an
apparently empty region of the night sky, just
to see what they could find.

Nearly every speck on this image is a galaxy
containing many millions or billions of stars.
There are only about a dozen foreground stars,
all residing in the Milky Way. They can be
spotted by the spikes of light that emanate
from them.

There are over a thousand galaxies in this
image and the colour of each provides a clue to
its distance: the further objects look redder
because of the redshift effect.

Deep fields show astronomers the very
distant universe and allow them to compare it
with the 'local' picture.

CAN REDSHIFTS BE RELIED UPON?

NGC 4319 AND MARKARIAN 205

Anomalous redshifts

A small number of astronomers do not believe in the redshift as an indicator of distance. In their view, redshift is not caused by the expanding universe but by some other, as yet unknown, process. They base their views on a number of peculiar galactic alignments that appear to show objects at very different redshifts (so very far apart according to the conventional interpretation) apparently interacting with one another.

One of the disputed systems is associated with the barred spiral galaxy NGC 4319. Next to it in the sky is another galaxy called Markarian 205. According to their redshifts, NGC 4319 is 80 million light years from Earth, while Markarian 205 is almost 14 times farther away, at around a billion light years.

The trouble is NGC 4319's dust lanes are clearly distorted, as if they are being influenced by a close neighbour. Some images of this pair also appear to show a faint bridge of matter running from one galaxy to the other.

This Hubble Space Telescope image, however, does not show the bridge and so most astronomers conclude that the apparent connection between Markarian 205 and NGC 4319 is simply an accident of their visual alignment and that the redshift–distance law still holds.

ECHO OF THE BIG BANG

THE COSMIC MICROWAVE BACKGROUND

Proof of the cosmic fireball

This image shows the whole sky and is a great triumph for astronomers because it captures the leftover radiation from the big bang itself. The so-called cosmic microwave background radiation can be thought of as the echo of the big bang. Where this radiation was once a seething fireball, at millions of degrees, it now warms the universe to just 2.7 degrees above absolute zero (–270 degrees Celsius).

The different colours represent the Doppler-shifted wavelengths of the micro-wave background. This is not caused by the expansion of the universe but by the movement of the Earth through space. Not only is the Earth orbiting the Sun but the Sun is also orbiting the centre of the Galaxy and the Galaxy is in motion towards the Great Attractor. This means that the micro-wave background appears blueshifted in one direction and redshifted in the other.

Contaminating microwaves from the plane of the Milky Way create the line across the centre of the image.

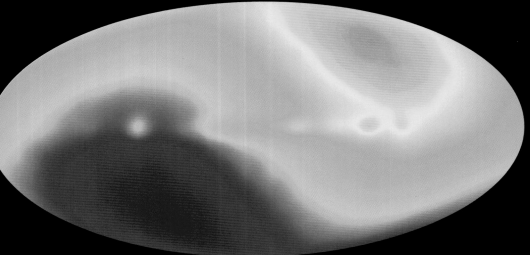

COSMIC INFLATION

How big got bigger

The extreme smoothness of the microwave background radiation has led cosmologists to wonder whether the universe went through a period of sudden expansion early in its history. This would have smoothed out any large-scale ripples in the cosmic microwave background radiation. Cosmologists call this hypothetical expansion 'inflation' but as yet they are not sure what drove the universe to behave in this way. If inflation is true it means that the universe we can see around us is just a small region of the true universe, as shown right.

Big Bang

Inflation

True extent of the universe

The observable
universe today

GRAVITY – ARCHITECT OF THE UNIVERSE

GRAVITY IS THE FORCE THAT DOMINATES THE COSMOS. IT NOT ONLY GUIDES CELESTIAL OBJECTS THROUGH THEIR ORBITS, BUT IT ALSO CONTROLS THEIR FORMATION BY DRAWING MATTER TOGETHER IN THE FIRST PLACE. THIS MAKES IT THE ARCHITECT OF THE UNIVERSE. GRAVITY BECAME DOMINANT ABOUT 300,000 YEARS AFTER THE BIG BANG. BEFORE THEN, THE UNIVERSE WAS SO HOT THAT THE ENERGY OF THE PARTICLES COULD OVERCOME GRAVITY'S GENTLE GRIP.

Gravity – architect of the universe

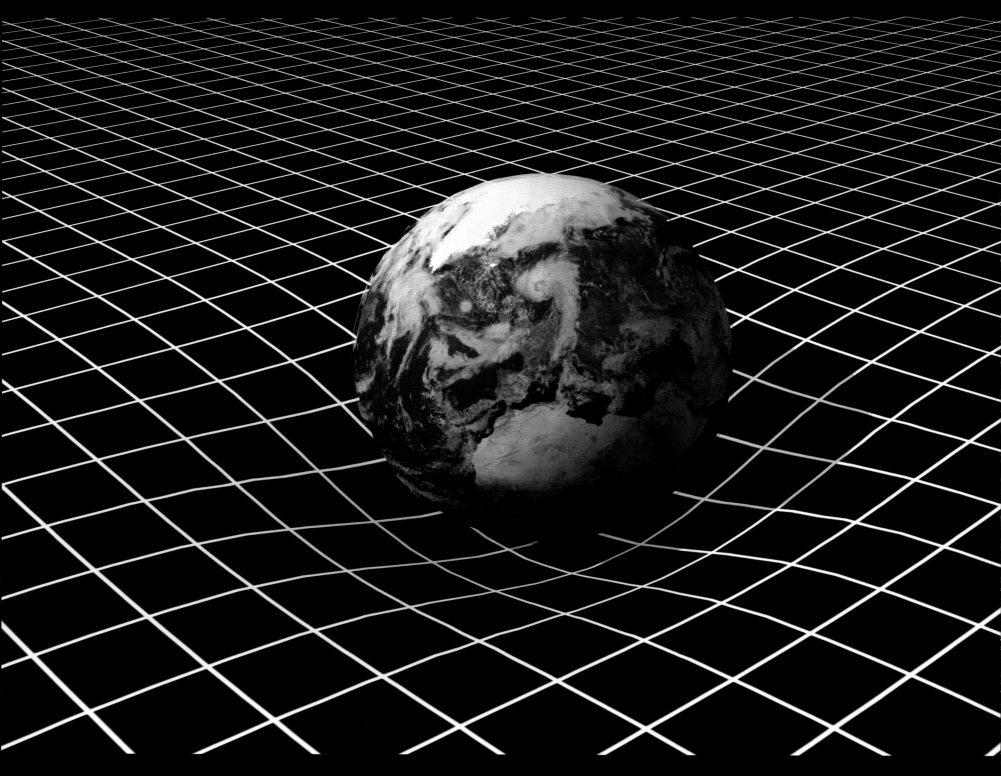

The clockwork universe

Isaac Newton formulated the first workable mathematical description of gravity, published in the *Principia* in 1687. In it he showed that the same force that causes objects to fall to the ground on Earth is also responsible for the movement of the planets in their orbits. His proof caused a revolution in thinking about the way the universe operated. For the first time, gravity was recognized as the key to the universe's motion.

Newton's work led to the idea that the universe was some sort of clockwork mechanism, with all movement being orchestrated by gravity. Because his laws described gravity, they could be used to predict the location of objects such as planets and comets. Astronomy changed at this point from

a science that struggled to explain what people saw into one that could predict certain future events. One of the earliest exponents of Newton's law of universal gravity was Edmond Halley, who used the equation to correctly predict the return of the comet named in his honour. Sadly, Halley died before it reappeared to prove him correct.

But Newton left one thing unexplained: what was gravity? He had correctly described the action of gravity with his mathematics but nowhere in his theory did he explain why it worked as it did.

Albert Einstein filled in this piece of the puzzle more than two hundred years later, in the early years of the 20th century, with his theory of general relativity. His great insight was to explain gravity as the result of the

curvature of the so-called spacetime continuum, the very fabric of space itself. Massive objects cause this to curve in the way a heavy ball placed on a rubber sheet will make it sag. Other objects feel this curvature as gravity. When objects are pulled together by gravity, they are actually falling down gravitational 'wells' in space.

To encapsulate this concept, Einstein developed a set of ten field equations. They describe how the presence of matter and energy causes space to curve and hence generate gravity. The Einstein field equations were first published in 1915.

General relativity made a unique prediction about the effect that spacetime curvature would have on light: it would be deflected. If starlight passed close to the Sun, the curvature of space

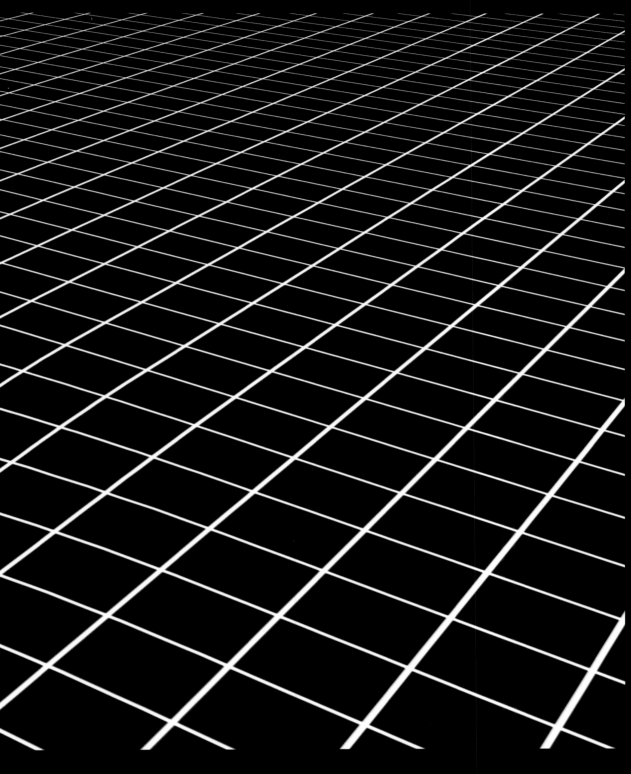

The curvature of space

According to general relativity, gravity is produced by the curvature of spacetime. The best way to think of this is as if space is a rubber sheet. Heavy objects cause this sheet to sag, producing a curved 'well' in which the object sits. Nearby smaller objects will also roll down the curve, falling into the well created by the heavy object. We cannot see this curvature but we perceive it through the motion of objects rolling down it. So, from our vantage point it looks as if one object has attracted the other. Gravity is the name we give to this force of attraction.

would deflect the light beam by a small amount. Astronomers realized that to measure the position of stars so close to the Sun they would have to wait for a total solar eclipse. As the Moon slipped in front of the fiery glare and the sky went dark, they would have a few minutes to photograph the scene. Later, they could measure the position of the stars on the photograph and check for the predicted deflection.

In 1919, British astrophysicist Arthur Eddington travelled to the island of Principe, off the west coast of Africa, where a solar eclipse had been predicted for 29 March. He and his team successfully captured photographs of the eclipse and announced that Einstein's predicted deflection was true. The story was carried across the world.

General relativity also predicted the expanding universe and, when Hubble proved that in 1929, the theory's position as the correct method of picturing the cosmos became unassailable.

Gravitational waves

Today, astronomers are endeavouring to detect a third prediction of general relativity. Gravitational waves are thought to flow in the fabric of spacetime, equivalent to ripples on a pond. These waves happen whenever something cataclysmic takes place in the universe, for example, the collision of two stars or the explosion of a massive star. They literally set the spacetime continuum quaking. As the ripples pass the Earth, sensitive equipment flexes one way and then the other. By detecting

this tiny movement, which is about one billion times smaller than the width of a typical atom, astronomers could gain a unique window on the universe, allowing them to probe violent events in more detail than they have ever achieved before.

As successful as it is, general relativity is not the final theory of gravity. There are a few chinks in its armour that hint that another – more complete – theory of gravity is waiting to be constructed. Physicists call this new theory quantum gravity and are working hard to formulate a complete, testable version. After decades of work, however, it is proving elusive.

SMALL-SCALE GRAVITY

BARNARD 68

Black cloud

Gravity is responsible for star formation by pulling together clouds of gas and dust. Inside these clouds, the temperature is so low that atoms can stick together and form molecules. Hence, astronomers call these molecular clouds. Barnard 68 is a dense molecular cloud about 500 light years away from Earth. It spans approximately half a light year.

Areas within this cloud are probably beginning to collapse even further, due to gravity, and they will eventually become stars. When these black clouds were first seen, we wondered whether they were holes in the Milky Way. American astronomer E.E. Barnard catalogued 366 dark nebulae and published his list in 1919. Now we know that these molecular clouds are so dense that the starlight from behind cannot pass through.

BOK GLOBULES

A string of black pearls

Nine and a half thousand light years away, a
string of black pearls hangs in front of the
glowing gas cloud, NGC 281. Stretching across
three light years, these globules are being
pulled together by gravity to become stars.
They are known as Bok globules after Dutch
astronomer Bart Bok who studied them during
the 20th century.

THACKERAY'S GLOBULES

Australia in space

Here, two Bok globules overlap in our line of
sight to produce a combined silhouette that
resembles the shape of Australia. They are 5900
light years away and their combined diameter
is 1.4 light years. Each globule is estimated to
hold a quantity of matter about 15 times the
mass of our Sun.

I04302

Young star and planet-forming disc

Eventually gravity builds a star and surrounds
it with a flat spinning disc of dusty matter. The
work of our architect does not always end
there: gravity then transforms this disc into
planets. In I04302, the light from the new star
illuminates surrounding gas clouds while the
thick disc of planet-forming material blocks out

LARGE-SCALE GRAVITY

Groups of galaxies

On a much larger scale than star formation, gravity holds whole galaxies together. This huge gravitational force spills out beyond their rims, allowing galaxies to hold on to one another. We call such collections groups or clusters of galaxies depending upon their respective sizes.

This is Hickson Compact Group 87, a collection of four galaxies, 400 million light years away. They are bound together and gravity is swinging them through their orbits. Because they are in close proximity to one another, each is being pulled by its neighbours. In effect, each galaxy is trying to orbit the other three. In situations like this, the chances of galactic collisions are high.

NGC 7318A, B, 7319, 7320
STEPHAN'S QUINTET

Interacting galaxies

The galaxies in Stephan's Quintet (left and far left), located 270 million light years away, are even more closely packed together. As a result, disconnected arms and errant dust lanes cross the image. These are sure signs of gravity's influence. The disconnected arms are called tidal tails. Just as the Moon's gravity creates the tides on the Earth, so the gravity of one galaxy causes tides in another. Instead of oceans though, it is thousands or even millions of stars that are pulled around. Sometimes they are pulled clean out of their parent galaxy to become tidal tails.

M65, M66, NGC 3628
THE LEO TRIPLET

This small group of galaxies forms a conspicuous trio in the constellation Leo. They are situated at a distance of about 35 million light years, and feel each other's pull of gravity. Long exposure photography reveals knots of star formation in the edge-on spiral galaxy, NGC 3628. These have been triggered by the gravity of the other galaxies.

GRAVITY'S DEFORMING HAND

M82 CIGAR GALAXY

Wracked by star formation

The Cigar Galaxy has been pulled out of any classifiable shape by the gravity of a nearby, larger galaxy. The strong gravitational force from the larger companion has triggered star formation in M82 at a rate ten times faster than usual.

The blue disc is the combined light of billions of hot, young stars. The dark clouds, silhouetted against this blazing stellar mass, have yet to be transformed into stars. The fountains of red gas were thrown out of the galaxy and are now raining back down to form even more stars. Astronomers call such frantic star formation a starburst.

Such encounters were more frequent in the early universe, when galaxies were more densely packed together, so many must have suffered M82's fate back then.

M81 BODE'S GALAXY

The tormentor of M82

It is M81 whose gravity is responsible for triggering the starburst in M82. The two galaxies almost collided 600 million years ago but at nearly twice the diameter of M82, Bode's Galaxy was little affected by their near miss. It maintains an orderly rate of star formation that proceeds in a spiral fashion around the central core. This shows up as red in this infrared image and reveals dust in the birth clouds surrounding the young stars.

M4

Freshly minted stars

More than 100 globular clusters have formed as a result of M82's brutal gravitational encounter with M81. This particular example, M4, orbits our own galaxy but is similar to the ones that now surround M82. It is 70 light years in diameter and contains in excess of 100,000 stars. Its existence may be telling astronomers that our own Milky Way once had as violent a past as M82.

WHEN GRAVITY BECOMES IRRESISTIBLE

NGC 2207 & IC 2163

Disaster ahead

Galaxies caught in each other's gravitational embrace are destined to collide and merge. Here, the large spiral galaxy NGC 2207, whose diameter is 143,000 light years, is about to engulf IC 2163.

This drama is playing out 115 million light years away, affording Earthly astronomers a grandstand view.

The smaller of the two galaxies is unravelling, due to the tides caused by the gravity of the larger neighbour. Because IC 2163 is so wide, about 101,000 light years, the gravitational force from NGC 2207 weakens across this distance, so stars on the smaller galaxy's near side are pulled harder than those farthest away. The nearside stars speed up while those on the far side lag behind and the galaxy slowly stretches out in space.

COLLIDING GALAXIES

NGC 4038 & NGC 4039
ANTENNAE GALAXIES

The fires of collision

The actual collision of two galaxies is a time of high drama, but played out in slow motion on a timescale of millions of years because of the vast size of the objects involved.

These two galaxies, NGC 4038 and NGC 4039, are 63 million light years away and are suffering a cataclysm. Their central stellar bulges show up as red stars but everything else is burning blue with the glow of new stars, triggered into formation by the gravitational mayhem of the collision.

At the point where the galaxies are 'touching', a massive pile-up of dust can be seen. As time goes by, this will fragment into billions of new stars and the Antennae will become a single, brilliant object, blazing into space. Following this huge starburst, we believe it will settle down to become a single, elliptical galaxy.

CLOSE-UP ON THE ANTENNAE

An X-ray view

X-ray image 1 reveals spectacular loops of multimillion-degree gas reaching out into intergalactic space. The bright points are neutron stars and black holes. The image is colour coded so that low-, medium- and high-energy X-rays appear as red, green and blue, respectively.

Image 2 shows a close-up of the central regions. The neutron stars and black holes have been digitally removed, leaving just the enormous gas clouds that have been heated by the titanic collision. Again, the colours reveal the energies of the X-rays.

Image 3 is coloured differently. This time it shows the distribution of chemical elements throughout the Antennae. Red, green and blue show regions rich in iron, magnesium and silicon respectively.

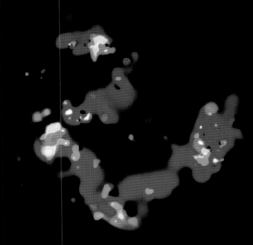

1

2

3

TIDAL TAILS

The real antennae

This wide-angle image of the Antennae Galaxies shows how they got their name. Both draw a tidal tail across space. These stars will probably never be incorporated into the merged galaxy. Instead, they have escaped its gravitational pull altogether and will now wander the depths of space on their own. The radio image (left) shows the gas in the tail as a blue sweep, whereas the optical image (bottom) shows the stars in the tail.

GRAVITATIONAL LENSES

H1413+117 CLOVERLEAF QUASAR

Far, far away

As extraordinary as it seems, gravity can also act as a magnifying lens. Einstein first realized this in 1912 and thought it might be the explanation for novae, which are now known to be exploding stars. Imagining that one star might pass in front of another, halfway between it and the Earth, Einstein understood that such an alignment would produce a magnification of the more distant star. This happens because the gravity of the intervening, or lensing, star bends light that would usually miss the Earth into our line of sight, temporarily increasing the object's brightness.

Einstein's further calculations, however, showed that such an alignment was highly unlikely and could not explain the dozens of novae that astronomers saw every year.

Then in the 1980s, astronomers found galaxies acting as gravitational lenses for more distant galaxies. Because the lensing galaxy is a complicated shape, this form of lens not only amplifies the light, it also splits it into multiple images. Usually the lensed galaxy is a bright form of distant galaxy called a quasar. The Cloverleaf Quasar in this particular image is 11 billion light years away and the unseen lensing galaxy lies at about half that distance. The four images are all of the same quasar.

SDSS J1004+4112

A lensed quasar

Surrounding the centremost orange galaxy are four, bright, star-like objects. The different images are of the same celestial object. They show a single quasar that lies directly behind the galaxy. The images have been split by the galaxy's gravity.

EINSTEIN RINGS

EIGHT GRAVITATIONAL LENSES

The hunt for perfect circles

The distortion of space caused by the presence of a large galaxy gives rise to its gravity and the ability for that gravity to act as a lens. If the alignment between the Earth, the lensing galaxy and the distant galaxy is perfect, general relativity predicts that the resulting images will not be split into individual images but instead they will be smeared into a continuous ring of light surrounding the lens.

These rings have been called Einstein rings and are highly sought after by astronomers because of their beauty. Since 1985, astronomers have discovered over 100 gravitational lenses. They have not yet, however, found a perfect Einstein ring at optical wavelengths. The nearest they have come are these arcs surrounding galaxies, each one about four billion light years away.

At radio frequencies, where the waves are much longer than in the optical part of the spectrum, Einstein rings can be seen.

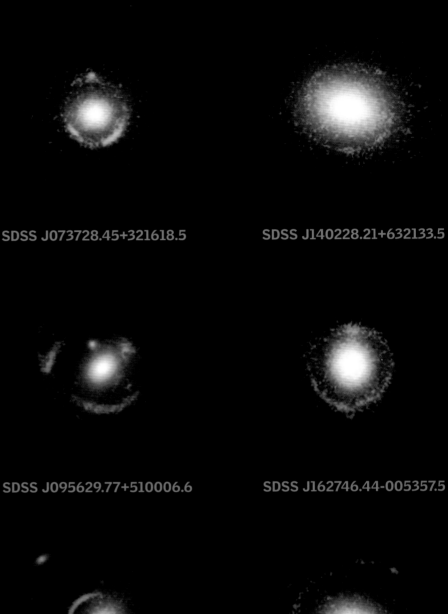

SDSS J073728.45+321618.5   SDSS J140228.21+632133.5

SDSS J095629.77+510006.6   SDSS J162746.44-005357.5

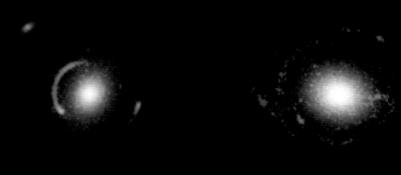

SDSS J120540.43+491029.3   SDSS J163028.15+452036.2

SDSS J125028.25+052349.0   SDSS J232120.93-093910.2

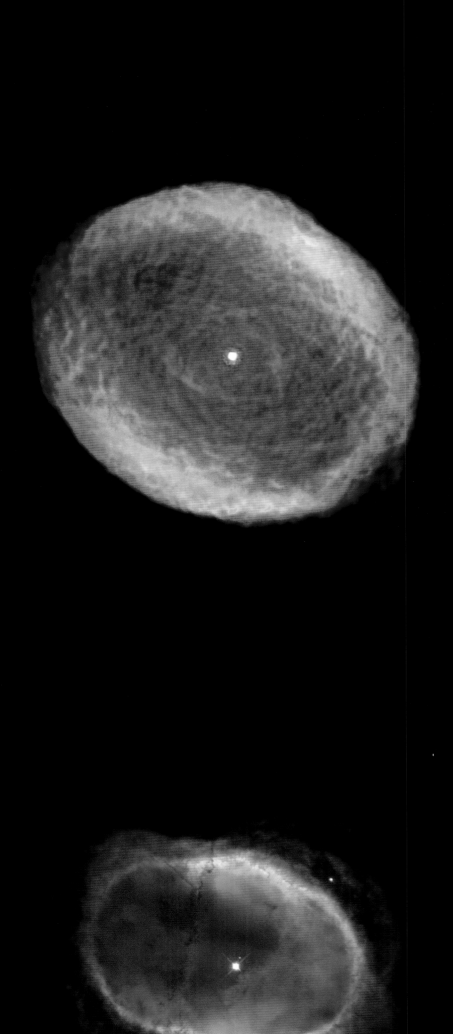

False alarm

Early false alarms, thought to be Einstein rings, were the round planetary nebulae. At first glance, it looked as if these fragile celestial rings were exactly what was sought but it soon became obvious that there were too many planetary nebulae, and they were too large, to be explained by the rare phenomenon of gravitational lensing.

NGC 3132

Eight burst nebula

Another planetary nebula that could be confused, on first sight, with an Einstein ring, NGC 3132 lies 2000 light years away and was created by a dying star ejecting its outer layers into space. The star that suffered this calamity is not the bright star in the centre but the faint companion.

CLUSTERS
AS LENSES

Abell 1689 GALAXY CLUSTER

Bigger gravitational lenses

Abell 1689 is one of the most massive galaxy clusters known. It seems to contain as much matter as 150 trillion suns. It is also the biggest magnifying lens in the universe. Spanning two million light years in diameter, we have found that it too acts as a gravitational lens. The graceful arcs that give this image a celestial spider's web appearance are the gravitationally lensed galaxies behind it.

Without Abell 1689 to act as a giant magnifying glass, we would never be able to see such distant and faint galaxies. Even so, the Hubble Space Telescope had to gaze in its direction for 13 hours to capture these faint wisps of light.

Not only does the gravitational lens reveal secrets of the distant universe, the arcs of light also tell astronomers how the mass is distributed inside the galaxy cluster. It seems that there is more mass inside the cluster than can be seen. Astronomers believe this could be in a form of exotic matter, unlike normal atoms. They call this dark matter (see Chapter 10).

BLACK HOLES AND ACTIVE GALAXIES

OF ALL THE AMAZING THINGS THAT GENERAL
RELATIVITY PREDICTED OR EXPLAINED, THE
STRANGEST IS THE CONCEPT OF THE BLACK HOLE.
IT IS SO OUTLANDISH THAT FOR MOST OF THE
MIDDLE DECADES OF THE 20TH CENTURY,
ASTRONOMERS AND GRAVITATIONAL PHYSICISTS
SPENT THEIR TIME TRYING TO PROVE THAT BLACK
HOLES COULD NOT EXIST.

Sheer cliffs in spacetime

A black hole is a three-dimensional object with such a strong gravitational field that it can capture and crush anything that strays too close. The critical distance to avoid is known as the event horizon. To all intents and purposes, the event horizon marks the extent of a black hole with its size determined by the black hole's mass. For example, a black hole containing the mass of the Earth would have a radius of a small coin, whereas one that contained billions of times more mass than the Sun would be as large as our solar system.

curved spacetime, a black hole produces such strong curvature that the gradient of spacetime becomes a sheer cliff. Nothing that falls in can ever expend enough energy to claw its way back out and so it becomes trapped forever.

As they worked at the calculations, astronomers realized that there was nothing in nature that could prevent their formation and so, gradually, they came to terms with the idea of black holes. However, they had another problem. How do you take an image of something that swallows everything that falls onto it – even light?

The solution came with the first X-ray

star associated with it. Could this be super-heated gas falling into a black hole? Astronomers believe so.

Black holes come in a variety of sizes. First, there are the stellar-sized black holes. These are like the one in Cygnus and contain several times the mass of the Sun. They are formed when massive stars explode.

Second, there is an intermediate class. These orbit the centres of galaxies, including ours, and contain a few hundred or thousand solar masses. Astronomers are not sure how these form; possibly they result from several stellar-sized black holes merging together.

Anatomy of a black hole
A black hole is not a simple object but is made of several parts.

Singularity
This is the point at which our laws of physics break down. Science cannot predict what happens at the singularity.

Event horizon
Surrounding the singularity is the region in which the curvature of spacetime is so severe that nothing can ever escape. Once an object crosses this event horizon, it can never return to the outside.

Ergosphere
If the black hole is spinning, it generates a slightly different gravitational force from that of a stationary black hole. In the ergosphere objects will be dragged around in the direction of the black hole's rotation.

Accretion disc
The accretion disc is a reservoir of hot matter, gradually spiralling to its doom.

Jets
Some of that matter in the accretion disc can actually escape falling over the event horizon and into the black hole. As well as gravity, there are powerful magnetic forces at play here. As the gas heats up, it becomes electrically charged, allowing it to interact with the magnetic field. As a result, some of the gas is lifted and thrown out into space in opposite directions as jets of matter.

mass of the Sun. A supermassive black hole is thought to sit in the centre of every galaxy. In most, the black hole is a sleeping giant but, in one in every ten galaxies it is driving some kind of extraordinary activity at the core.

Intergalactic searchlights
Massive quantities of radiation are released in these so-called active galaxies, all of it derived from interactions between matter and the central supermassive black hole. Astronomers believe that all active galaxies are fundamentally similar objects, which can be divided into a number of different classes.

There are the radio galaxies. These are often elliptical galaxies in which the tremendous forces at work in the core are squirting two jets of matter away from oblivion and out into the depths of intergalactic space, where they behave like gigantic searchlights and illuminate great clouds of intergalactic gas.

Then there are Seyfert galaxies. These are spirals with unusually bright cores. About two percent of all spirals display some form of Seyfert activity. It manifests itself primarily as highly energetic gas in the centre of the galaxy.

The most powerful of all the active galaxies are the quasars and their brighter cousins, the blazars. The cores of these galaxies are so bright that they outshine their surrounding galaxy. At first astronomers assumed they were looking at peculiar stars in our own galaxy. They called them quasi-stellar objects, from which the name is derived.

The mystery of the quasars' true nature was resolved when astronomers realized that they had incredibly large redshifts. Calculating their distances, we discovered that quasars populated the universe in their greatest abundance around ten billion years ago. Nowadays, there are no quasars in the universe. This brings us to the conclusion that quasars, and all the other forms of active galaxy, are phases that every galaxy passes through.

The mayhem in an active galaxy eventually dies down because the supermassive black hole has eaten everything within its grasp. When this has happened, the galaxy becomes normal. This raises the possibility that a galactic collision could reignite the amazing activity in a currently quiescent galaxy.

BLACK HOLES FROM SUPERNOVAE

Spiralling to destruction

The stellar-sized black hole of Cygnus X-1 lies 8000 light years away. We can only detect its presence because it is ripping its companion star, HDE 226868, to pieces. HDE 226868 is a blue supergiant star, about 30 times more massive than the Sun and 400,000 times brighter.

Astronomers have calculated that the black hole contains between five and ten times the mass of the Sun. Its gravitational field had pulled the blue supergiant into an egg-shape and is now gradually stripping it of gas. As this gas falls from the giant star it briefly enters a spiral orbit around the black hole, rather like water spiralling down a plughole. During this plunge, the gas heats up to millions of degrees and emits X-rays into space. We can detect such X-rays and use them to pinpoint the location of a black hole, as shown in the image below. The main image is an artist's impression of what must be taking place in Cygnus X-1.

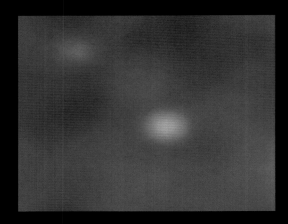

CASSIOPEIA A

The creation of a black hole

Stellar-sized black holes are thought to result from the explosion of a supergiant star at the end of its life. Such an explosion is called a supernova and although most of the star is blown into space, a core of four or more solar masses can collapse into a black hole. We can see evidence for a number of supernovae having taken place in the Milky Way over the last few centuries. This is the 300-year-old remnant of a star that exploded in the constellation of Cassiopeia.

HINTS OF SUPERMASSIVE
BLACK HOLES

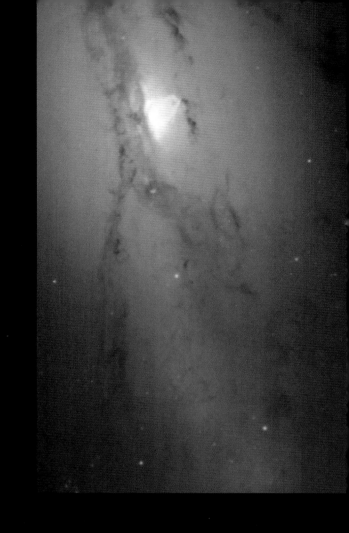

NGC 3079

Star formation or black hole?

Something in the heart of NGC 3079 is blowing huge pillars of gas out of the galaxy's core. Each towering pillar of gas is 2000 light years in length and 75 light years wide. The temperature of the gas is around 10 million degrees Celsius and by measuring the Doppler effect on this gas, we have found that it is moving at 6 million kph (4 million mph). As fast as this seems, it is still not enough to escape the galaxy entirely. Instead, the gas will eventually rain back down onto the galaxy, where its impact will catalyze the next generation of star formation.

Computer processing has made the starlight look green, while glowing gas shows up as red. The cause of the gaseous pillars is thought to be either the result of a burst of star formation at the centre of this galaxy or, less likely, gas escaping from the clutches of a supermassive black hole.

NGC 4438

Black hole sighted

We are certain that this bubble, in galaxy NGC 4438, is the result of gas escaping from a black hole. The plume is 800 light years long, while the galaxy itself lies at a distance of 50 million light years from Earth.

AN ACTIVE GALAXY

M87

Jet of doom

There can be no doubt here that a black hole's environment generates this extraordinary jet of matter in the giant elliptical galaxy M87. With a diameter of over 120,000 light years and at a distance of 60 million light years away, the galaxy was discovered by Charles Messier on 18 March 1781. At first sight it looks like nothing more than an elliptical galaxy. This view changed in 1918 when Heber D. Curtis of the Lick Observatory, California, successfully photographed the galaxy's central regions and discovered the jet emanating from the galaxy's heart. Between 7000 and 8000 light years long, the jet contains the remnants of stars and planets that have been ripped to pieces by the gravity of the central black hole.

As the destroyed objects fall towards the black hole they release energy which stirs up a giant vortex of matter and magnetic fields. Some of the matter tunnels along the magnetic fields to freedom. In doing so, it is reduced to subatomic particles and squeezed into jets.

The black hole responsible for this mayhem sits at the heart of the galaxy. It already contains as much matter as around two billion suns and the jet shows that it is still feeding.

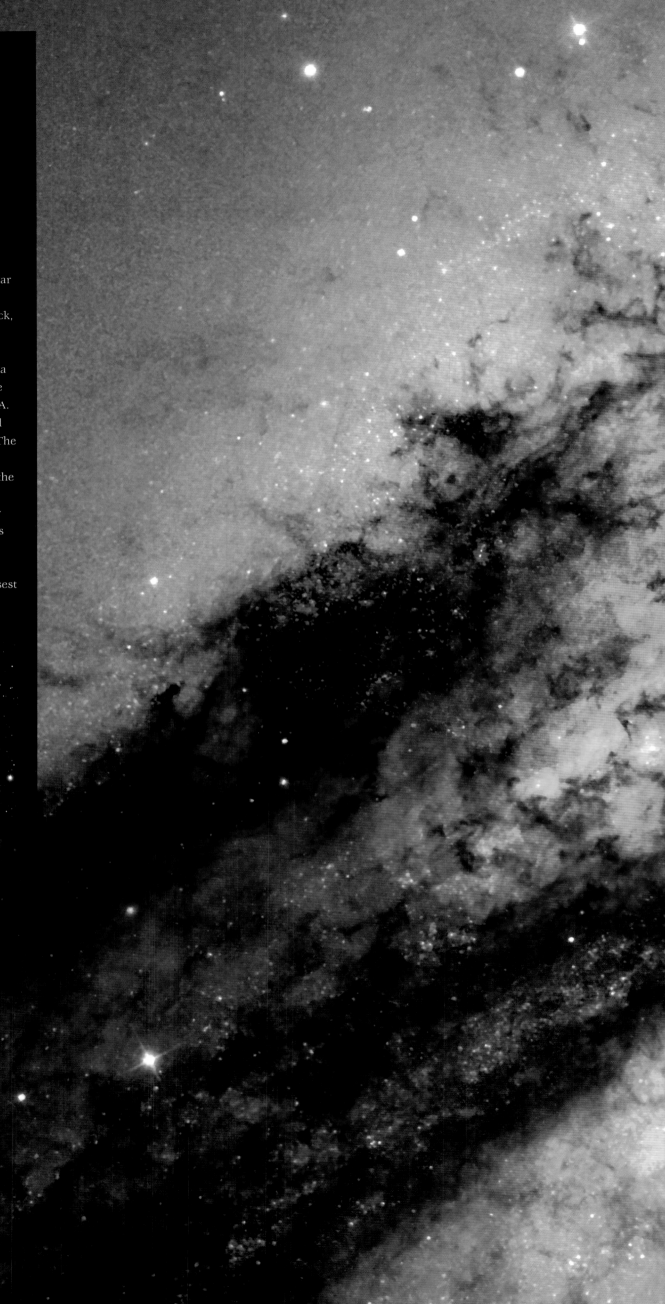

A SPIRAL MEETS AN ELLIPTICAL GALAXY

CENTAURUS A

Mighty collision

Unlike M87, there is no disguising the peculiar nature of Centaurus A. The enormous dust lane, running across its centre like a tyre track, is an immediate indicator that this galaxy is highly active.

The dust lane is the visible remainder of a spiral galaxy that ploughed headlong into the elliptical galaxy that has become Centaurus A. This massive merger is supplying the central black hole with enough food to gorge itself. The dust is also blocking our direct view of this feeding frenzy. The heart of Centaurus A is the yellow core in the image.

At radio wavelengths huge lobes, another certain indicator of a feeding black hole in its centre, surround Centaurus A. Best of all for astronomers, Centaurus A is located just 15 million light years away, so is one of the closest active galaxies to Earth.

RADIO GALAXIES

FORNAX A

Radio lobes

The enormous radio lobes, emanating from an active galactic nucleus, dwarf the entire host galaxy. This is radio galaxy Fornax A. Its orange radio lobes are one million light years across and overwhelm the actual galaxy, NGC 1316, sitting in the bright centre.

The orange colour is not real as these tremendous lobes are not visible to our eyes.

Instead they are picked up by radio telescopes and then colour coded by computers. The swirling patterns within the lobes are real, however. They are carved into the sky in that way because the jet from the black hole is wobbling slightly. It is similar to how a garden hose sprays water around at random when dropped.

The radio lobes themselves are generated when the ejected jets of matter collide with ambient gas within the incredibly rarefied reaches of intergalactic space.

NGC 1316

The galaxy within

This is the galaxy that sits at the heart of Fornax A. It is a peculiar elliptical galaxy in the process of swallowing a smaller spiral galaxy. Just as with Centaurus A, we are watching galactic activity spurred by a merger. The dust lanes are all that remain of the original spiral galaxy.

CYGNUS A

First radio galaxy

This was the first radio galaxy discovered. At 600 million light years away, it remains the most powerful radio galaxy known to astronomers. Two oppositely directed jets reach out across half a million light years to illuminate a pair of giant radio lobes. The galaxy itself is the bright blob approximately halfway between the two lobes.

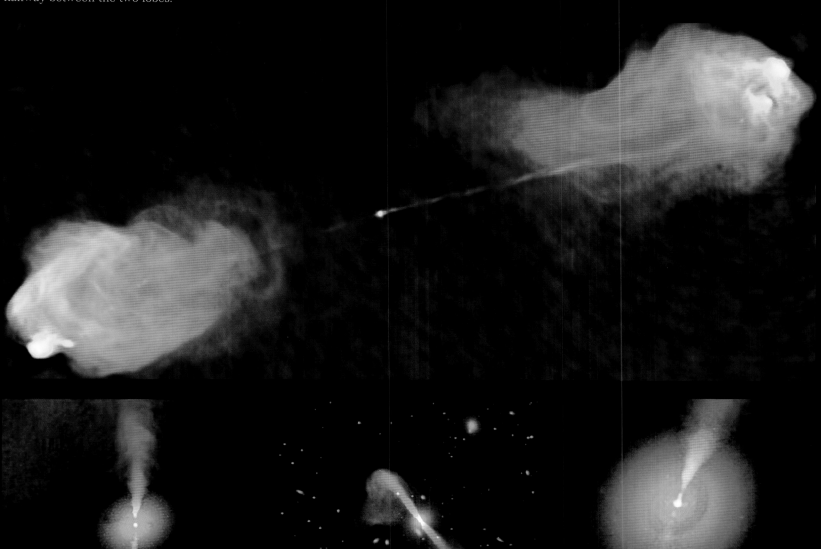

3C272.1

By any other name

To radio astronomers, the elliptical galaxy M84 is known as radio source 3C272.1. The galaxy lies 60 million light years away, in the Virgo cluster of galaxies. It is a neighbour of another active galaxy, M87.

3C296

Hidden giant

This radio galaxy hides at optical wavelengths within the elliptical galaxy, NGC 5532. The blue colour in this processed image shows the distribution of stars in the galaxy. The red jets show the subatomic particles spewing out into space, propelled by the tremendous forces at play close to the central black hole.

NGC 383

Wavering jets

Located 230 million light years from Earth, NGC 383 contains a supermassive black hole that forces jets of matter across almost a million light years, creating the radio source 3C31. Further from the galaxy, the jets are sweeping out great curves across space, indicating that something is causing them to wobble.

SEYFERT GALAXIES

ESO 97-G13

Spiral of death

Carl Seyfert identified this class of unusual spiral galaxy in 1943. He realized that those spiral galaxies displaying unusually bright cores were the same as those with highly energetic gas in their centres.

The Circinus is a typical Seyfert galaxy. It is located 13 million light years away and spans 37,000 light years in diameter. As in all active galaxies, Circinus plays host to a feeding black hole. As gas spirals into the monster's clutches, it is heated by friction to many millions of degrees. This extra energy ejects some of the gas. The escaped particles are shown here as magenta streamers, suspended some 3000 light years above the active core.

M77

The nearest Seyfert

Seyfert galaxy M77 (above), otherwise known as NGC 1068, is special to astronomers. At a distance of about 60 million light years, it is the nearest Seyfert galaxy to Earth. Even before its recognition as an active galaxy, M77 was famous for being the second galaxy to have its redshift measured by Vesto Slipher.

The comparative proximity of the galaxy has allowed us to peer deeply into its active core. What we have found is that the disc of matter surrounding the black hole is inclined to our line of sight by 51 degrees and contains a mind-boggling 27 billion solar masses. The overall galaxy is gigantic, containing a trillion solar masses.

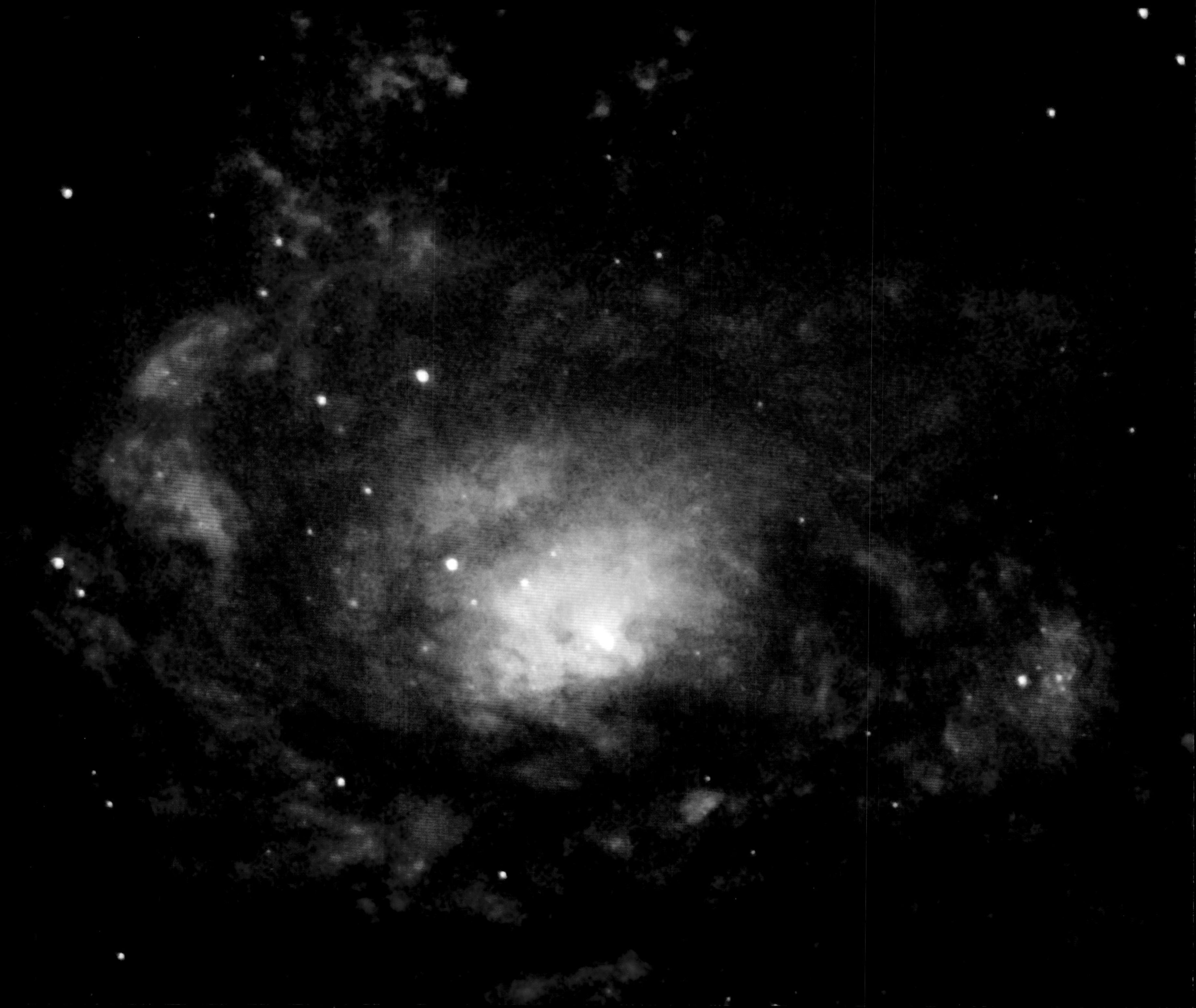

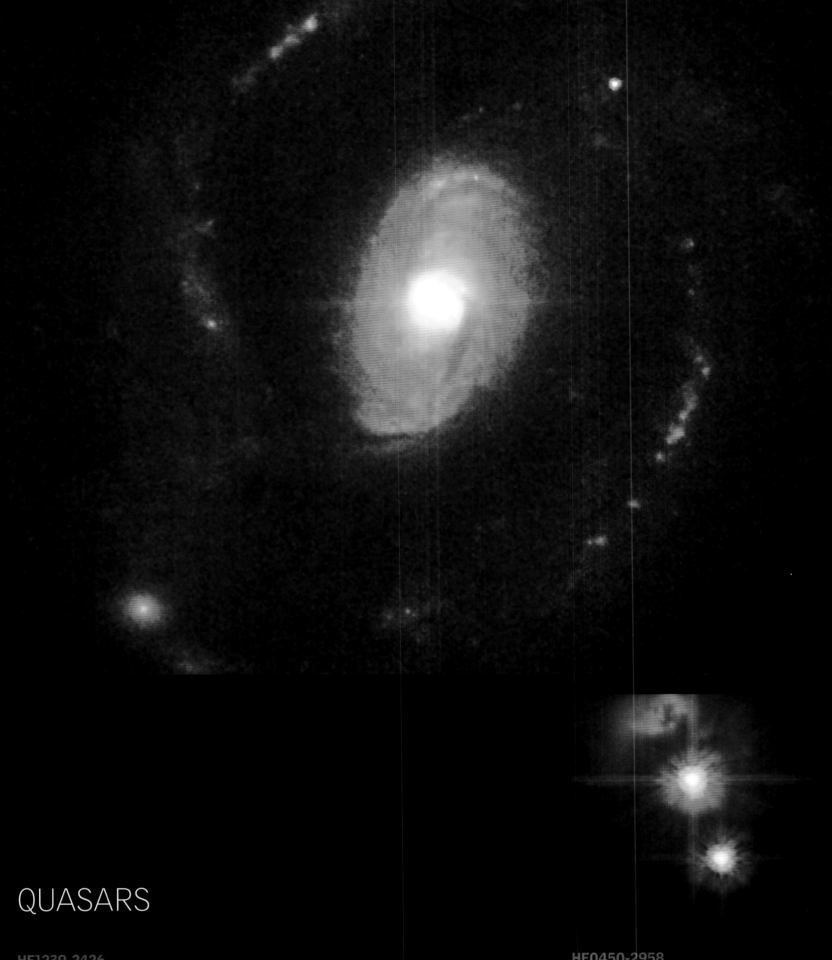

QUASARS

What feeds the monster?

Quasars are the most luminous of the active galaxies. They are not found in the universe today but live in the past, their numbers peaking at a redshift of between two and three, which corresponds to when the universe was about one-quarter of its present age.

It was only after the launch of the Hubble Space Telescope that we were able to glimpse the galaxies in which quasars sit. What we saw were galaxies similar to those of today but mostly being fed by some kind of tremendous merger.

Here, the host galaxy of HE1239-2426 (top)

is revealed to be a relatively normal-looking spiral galaxy. It is much closer than most quasars, at only 1.5 billion light years away. The brightness of an active galactic nucleus is driven by the amount of matter the black hole is eating. The greedier it gets, the brighter the galaxy becomes. Most quasars are assumed to be fed by merging galaxies although there is no obvious sign of that here. Perhaps the colliding galaxy is very small and so does not disturb the spiral pattern in this particular galaxy.

Where's the galaxy gone?

This is a naked quasar. Located five billion light years away, astronomers can find no trace of a host galaxy around this particular active galaxy. Instead it shows as a single star-like point in the centre of the image. The foreground star below it, illustrates the superficial similarity quasars share with stars. The nebulosity above the quasar is a foreground galaxy. Astronomers speculate that perhaps this quasar was formed when a supermassive black hole struck a small infant galaxy and we are watching it being eaten virtually whole.

A QUESTION OF VIEWPOINT

THE UNIFIED THEORY OF ACTIVE GALAXIES

One and the same?

We believe that the middle of each active galaxy follows essentially the same blueprint, called an active galactic nucleus. At the very centre of the galaxy sits the supermassive black hole. A swirling disc of gas surrounds the equator of the black hole. This gas is in the final stages of being swallowed up and, as it nears the event horizon, it speeds to thousands of kilometres, or miles, per second and releases a welter of X-rays that heat the active galactic nucleus.

Some of the gas is lifted by the magnetic fields at play in the centre of the galaxy and thrown out into space in opposite directions, creating the jets of matter. They travel so fast that they escape the gravitational influence not only of the black hole but of the galaxy too. Surrounding this disc and the black hole is a larger doughnut of dust and gas called the torus. Depending upon our viewing angle from Earth, the torus can obscure the active nucleus. This is how astronomers think the different classes of active galaxies came to be defined, not because there is an intrinsic difference in active galaxies but because of the different angles from which we see them.

When viewed edge-on, the active core is hidden from view but the jets are clearly visible. In this situation, we see a radio galaxy. If the galaxy is tilted and we can see both the jets and the bright core, we see a Seyfert galaxy or a quasar, depending upon how much energy is released in the core. Finally, if the active core is pointing straight at us, we see a super-bright quasar, called a blazar.

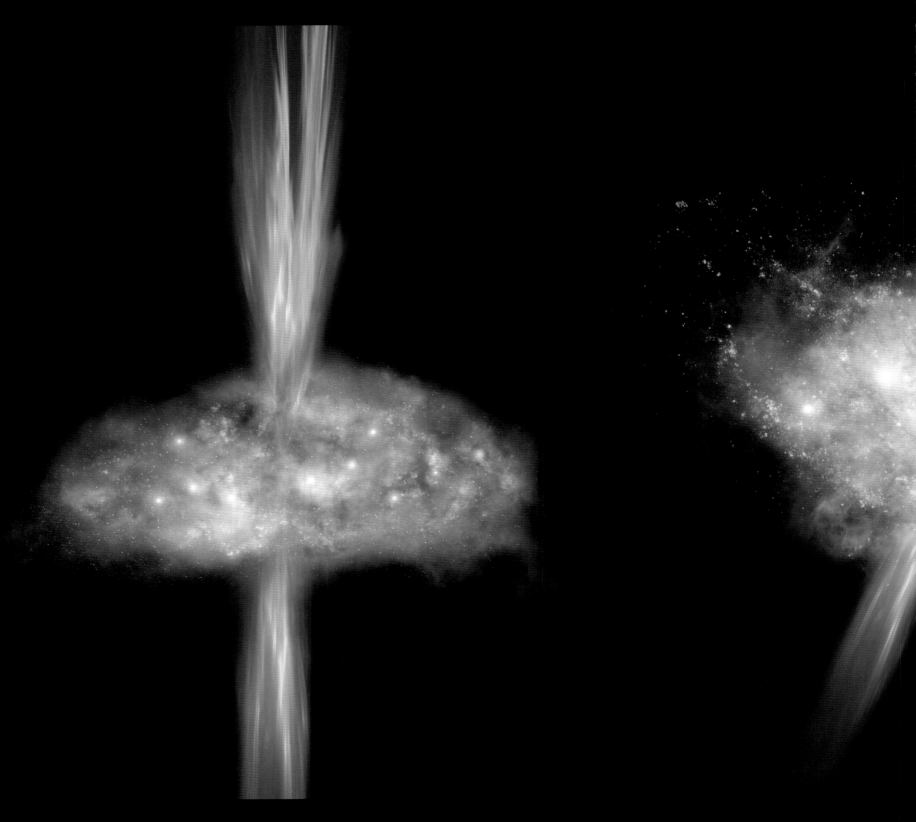

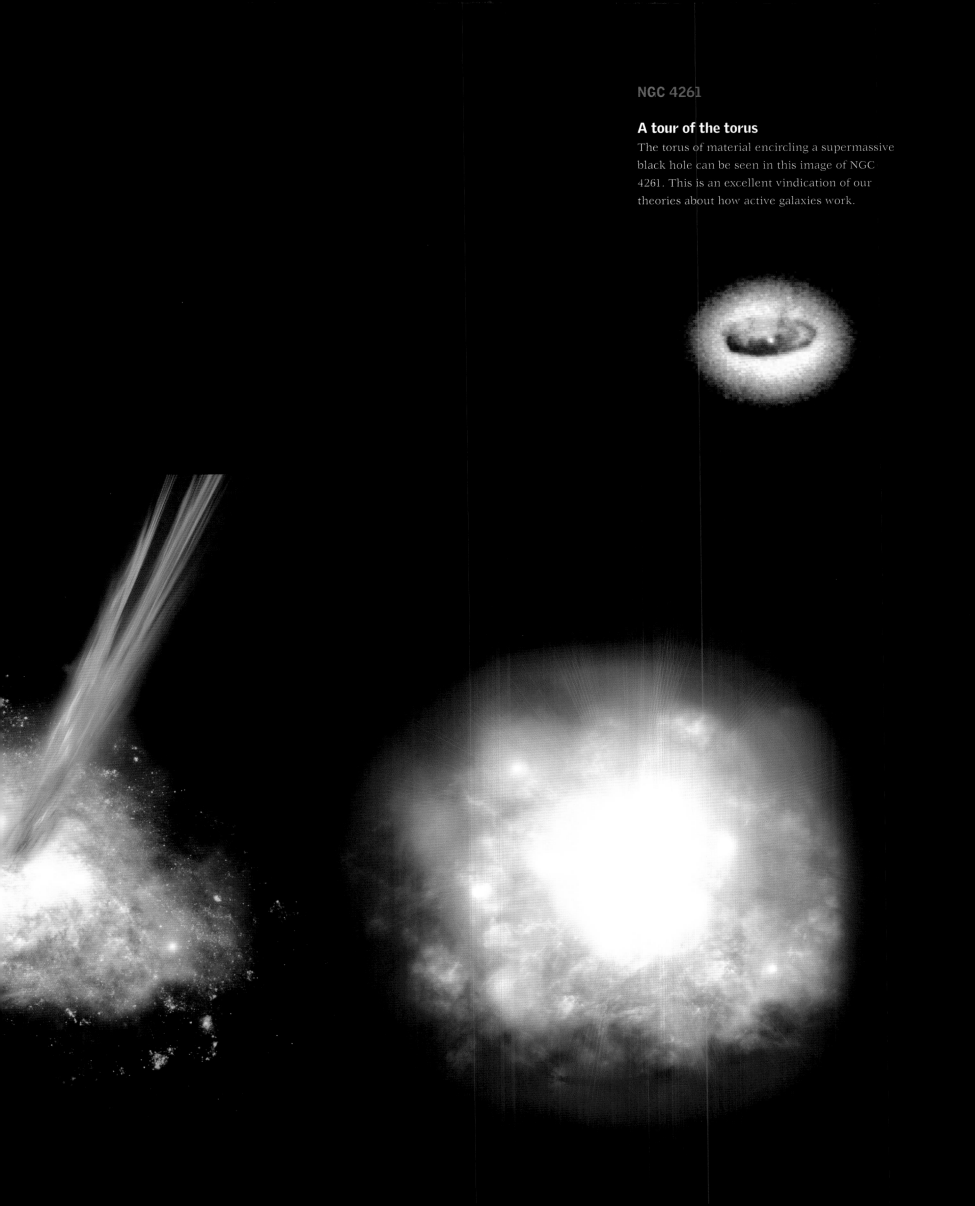

NGC 4261

A tour of the torus
The torus of material encircling a supermassive black hole can be seen in this image of NGC 4261. This is an excellent vindication of our theories about how active galaxies work.

DEVOURED BY A SUPERMASSIVE BLACK HOLE

PERSEUS A

Scything through a galaxy

The curving dust lanes of the incoming spiral galaxy can just be made out in this image of radio galaxy Perseus A. It is cutting through the heart of an elliptical galaxy. Both galaxies are 50,000 light years across and are colliding with a combined speed of 10 million kph (6 million mph).

almost at the centre of the cluster, dominating any galaxy that strays too close.

It is another strong piece of evidence that active galactic nuclei can only be present in merging systems. In such systems, the collision forces matter into the centre of the galaxy where the black hole resides, providing it with food.

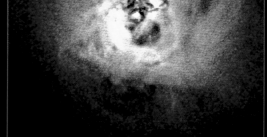

A song from space

The chaotic environment around the Perseus A black hole creates oscillations in the density of the gas. These oscillations are simple sound waves, and so astronomers can work out the musical note that Perseus A is singing. It is a guttural B flat, in the 57th octave below middle C. How low can you go?

Powered by gravity

Falling into a black hole is one of the most efficient ways to produce energy in the universe. The vast power coming out of this galaxy's centre is proof. Up to fifty percent of an object's mass can be converted into energy and radiated across space as it plunges into oblivion. By way of comparison, the nuclear fusion that keeps stars alive is less than one percent efficient.

In this X-ray image of the elliptical galaxy NGC 4696, 150 million light years away, the superheated gas shines across space.

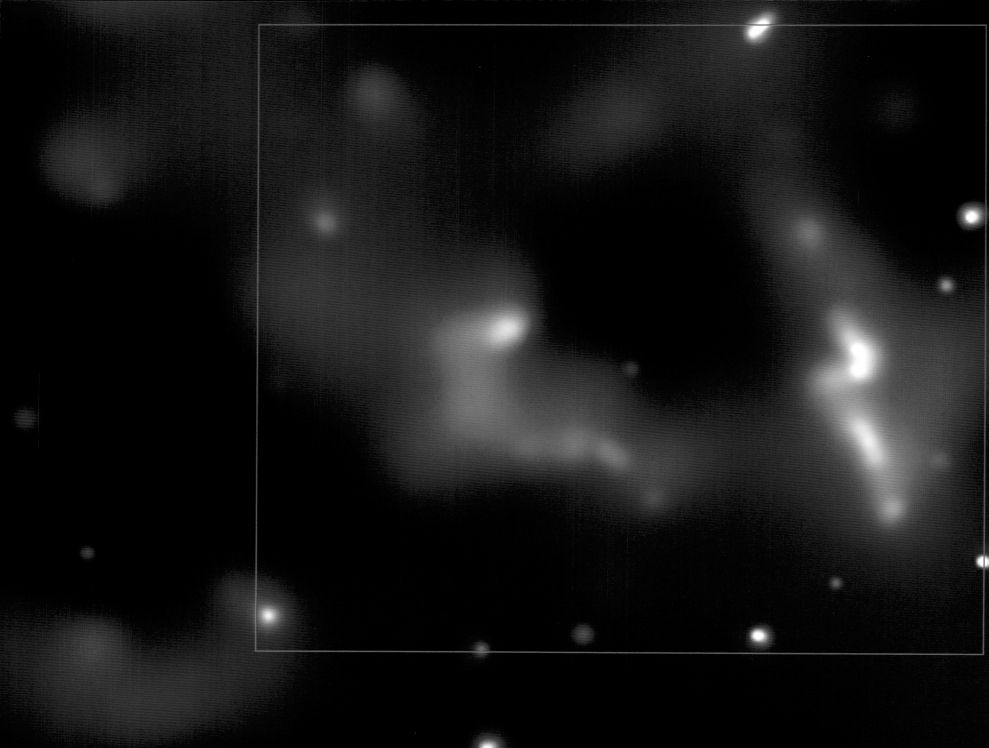

BLACK HOLES IN EVERY GALAXY?

SAGITTARIUS A*

The X-ray echo of a black hole

The triggering of activity in a galaxy by a merger suggests that a black hole is simply waiting at the core for its next meal. When it eats, it flares into violent activity but when it has finished, it lapses into quiescence. In the past, the universe was smaller and therefore more crowded, so collisions were more frequent and the incidence of active galaxies was higher. As the universe expanded, the collisions were fewer and more galaxies became quiescent.

Astronomers do believe that there remains a supermassive black hole at the heart of every galaxy.

Using X-ray telescopes, we can monitor the activity of Sagittarius A*, the black hole in the centre of the Milky Way. This image shows a sudden brightening of two clouds about 50 light years away from the black hole's location. We think that the clouds have acted as mirrors and bounced X-rays into our direction. The radiation was produced when the black hole ate something

containing the same mass as Mercury.

If matter were to start falling continuously into Sagittarius A* again, it would turn our galaxy into a Seyfert galaxy, which would flood space with radiation. Thankfully, astronomers can see no obvious reservoirs of matter than could make this happen.

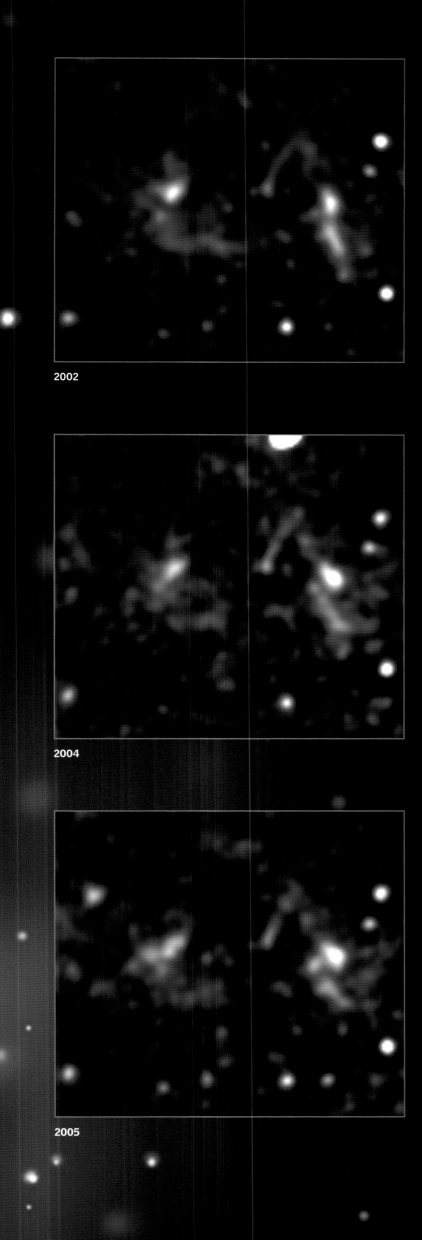

2002

2004

2005

STARS

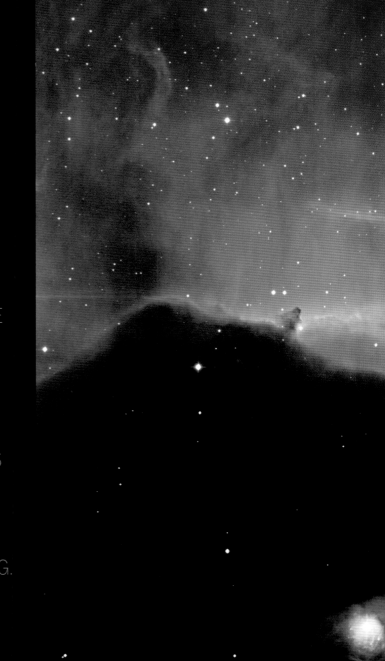

TODAY, ASTRONOMERS ARE IN COMPETITION WITH ONE ANOTHER TO SEE WHO CAN DETECT THE FIRST STARS THAT SHONE OUT INTO SPACE. NO ONE HAS YET SEEN THESE OBJECTS BECAUSE THEY ARE LOCATED SO FAR AWAY. CALCULATIONS SUGGEST THAT THE FIRST STARS MUST BE OVER 13 BILLION LIGHT YEARS AWAY AND MUST HAVE BEEN BORN SOMETIME BETWEEN 200 MILLION AND ONE BILLION YEARS AFTER THE BIG BANG.

The first stars

Of all the celestial objects, stars are the ones that have the biggest say over the chemical composition of the universe. And none affected it more than the first stars. They are believed to have been different from any we have yet seen in the universe. Bigger than any present stars, they would have contained between one hundred and one thousand times the amount of gas in our own Sun. Each one would be large enough to engulf all the planets in the solar system, if it were to be placed at the Sun's location.

The chemical universe

These early megastars were the chemical factories of the universe. Before they existed, the only chemicals found in space were the two lightest gases: hydrogen and helium. The megastars, with their vast internal nuclear furnaces, transformed a small fraction of the hydrogen and helium into the other chemical elements. At the end of their short lives, which perhaps lasted just a few million years each, they exploded and scattered their internal chemicals into space.

Amazingly, although they have not seen the stars, astronomers may have glimpsed the final explosions. As befits gargantuan stars, each one dies with a titanic outburst that releases as much energy as ten million billion Suns. This energy is packed into a sudden burst of gamma rays that reaches all the way to the other side of the universe. Having taken many billions of years to travel across the universe, these sudden bursts of gamma rays now arrive from any direction, completely without warning.

They are fleeting and last just a few seconds.

We have puzzled for decades over gamma ray bursts but now, using highly sophisticated spacecraft that are sensitive to this radiation, these explosions can be pinpointed and other telescopes guided to the correct location within seconds. The observations convince astronomers that we are seeing huge stars explode in the early universe.

The explosions seeded the cosmos with everything it needed to form the next generation of stars. This time the stars were made not just of hydrogen and helium, but also of heavier elements such as oxygen, carbon and silicon. These helped the stars to form faster and so prevented them from accumulating so much gas. As a result, the subsequent stars were smaller and burned their

Which came first?

Today, stars are overwhelmingly found in galaxies. Does this mean that the first stars formed in vast pockets of gas can be thought of as the first galaxies? Or did isolated stars form at random and then pull themselves together through gravity to form galaxies?

The answer to this question is important because, if galaxies formed first, then the first light to shine across the universe might not have come from the first stars. Instead, each galaxy may have begun with a central black hole. As the black hole's overwhelming gravity pulled the surrounding gas to its doom, the gas will have travelled faster and faster, heating up until it reached millions of degrees. At such extreme temperatures, the gas would radiate not just light but intensely powerful X-rays and gamma rays into the universe. When this happened, the galaxies would become smaller versions of the powerful active galaxies that astronomers call quasars (see Chapter 6). Only after this would stars begin to form.

If stars form first:

1. Small clouds of gas collapse across the universe.
2. The first stars are born and shine into space.
3. Gravity pulls the first stars together.
4. The stars cluster and become the first galaxies; their combined gravity pulls in gas from the surroundings.

If galaxies form first:

5. Large clouds of gas collapse across the universe.
6. Black holes form at the centres of these forming galaxies.
7. The black holes begin eating gas from their surroundings.
8. Eventually, stars begin to form in the galaxies.

hydrogen fuel more slowly. Thus they lived longer than their earlier cousins. Most stars today live for billions of years before releasing their chemical products back into space.

We estimate that there have been at least three generations of stars in the universe. Each subsequent generation has enriched the cosmos with heavy elements, including metallic substances such as iron and nickel, but it is a slow process. The stars have been doing their work in the cosmos for around 13 billion years, yet to date they have converted just two percent of the universe's hydrogen and helium into the heavier chemical elements.

Heavy elements are crucial because they allow planets to form. The core of each planet is a dense ball of metallic alloy and the overlying rocks are made from silicon. In the case of the Earth, the carbon produced in those earlier stars has formed the molecules that make life possible. We would love to know if this has happened elsewhere in the cosmos but as yet telescopes are not powerful enough to see sufficient detail on planets around other stars.

There seems to be nothing in the laws of science that prevents life from forming on other planets. However, we have not yet been able to understand precisely how life developed on Earth from inanimate chemicals, so are unsure of the necessary conditions. Understanding the origin of life is one of science's greatest quests.

The nature of the first objects to shine in the universe also determines how easy it would be for subsequent objects to form. Light and other radiation released by the first stars and black holes create turbulence in the surrounding gas. The more turbulent the gas, the harder gravity has to work to pull the celestial objects together, and so the more slowly would new stars form. We think that the development of small quasars, rather than huge stars, would slow down the star formation process.

Only by building incredibly powerful telescopes, to peer back into these ancient realms, will we be able to answer the questions about the first celestial objects. Until then, by studying the nearer stars, we continue to gain valuable insights into the workings of the first stars and the crucial role they played in preparing the universe for its subsequent development.

IMAGINING THE FIRST STARS

THE FIRST STARS AND GALAXIES

The sky ablaze with celestial fires

At present, when trying to picture what the first stars and clusters looked like, all we have to go on is our imagination and the appearances of nearby star clusters and nebulae. We believe that the early universe would have looked very different from today. Instead of the calm sea of more-or-less sedate galaxies, the sky would have been ablaze with the fires of cosmic dawn.

This artist's impression shows how the universe might have looked during the first billion years following the big bang. Back then the universe was going through the voracious onset of star formation, converting its primordial hydrogen into myriad stars at an unprecedented rate.

The galaxies are all irregular starburst galaxies because elliptical and spiral galaxies have not yet had time to form. Within the starburst galaxies, bright knots of massive stars come and go in a matter of a few million years, each giant star exploding in a titanic supernova.

A foreground starburst galaxy, at the lower right of the picture, is sculpted with hot bubbles from supernovae and torrential stellar winds. Hydrogen gas clouds glow red under the intense ultraviolet radiation released by these stars.

Also missing are the dark lanes seen in present-day galaxies. This is because the stars have yet to form large quantities of the heavier chemical elements that are necessary to create dust.

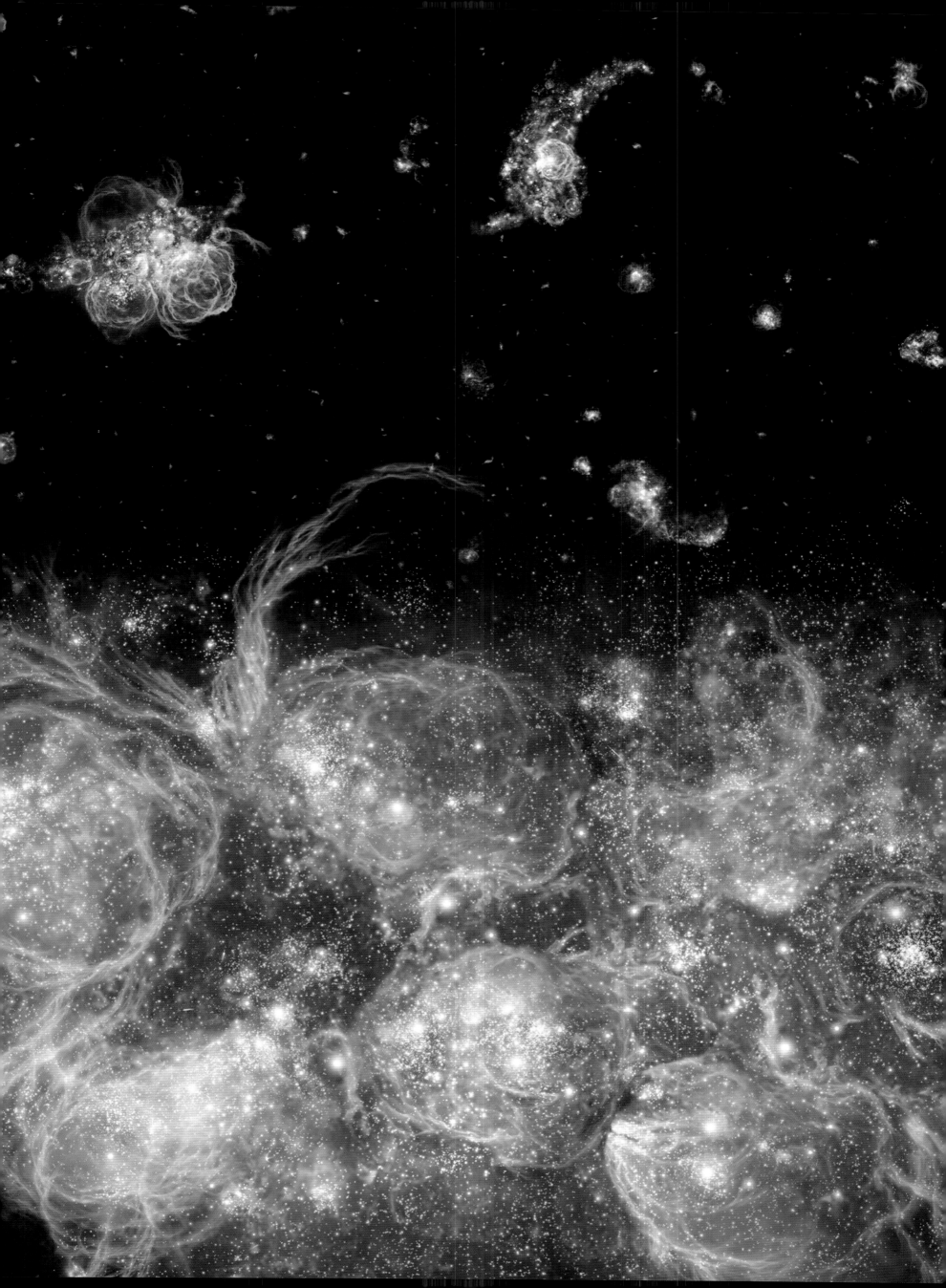

OUT OF THE DARKNESS

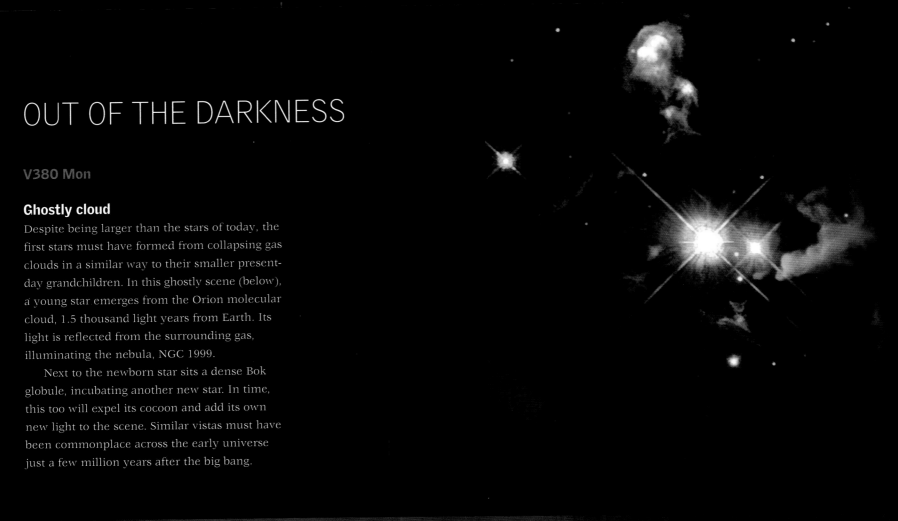

V380 Mon

Ghostly cloud

Despite being larger than the stars of today, the first stars must have formed from collapsing gas clouds in a similar way to their smaller present-day grandchildren. In this ghostly scene (below), a young star emerges from the Orion molecular cloud, 1.5 thousand light years from Earth. Its light is reflected from the surrounding gas, illuminating the nebula, NGC 1999.

Next to the newborn star sits a dense Bok globule, incubating another new star. In time, this too will expel its cocoon and add its own new light to the scene. Similar vistas must have been commonplace across the early universe just a few million years after the big bang.

HH 32

Shocking birth

Instead of emerging from dusty cocoons, the massive newborns of the early universe simply burst onto the scene. On a smaller scale it still happens today and the young star in the centre of this image (left) has caused shock waves (shown in green) to ripple through the remains of the gas cloud.

NGC 2261

Emerging star R Monocerotis

Young stars today are enswathed not just in gas but in dust as well. These dusty cocoons are gradually eroded by the radiation from the newborn sun. This young star, 2500 light years from Earth, has hollowed out a cone in the surrounding cloud, like a chick pecking the first hole in its surrounding egg.

In the early universe, structures such as this were probably missing because there were no heavier elements to form dust. Only after the first generation of stars did cosmic dust become a possibility.

STAR CLOUDS

N11B

Clusters of young stars

The very first stars lived short, furious lives and swiftly seeded space with the heavy chemical elements necessary to make dust. So, star formation rapidly became a dust-laden affair.

The dust grains act as a coolant, dissipating heat from gas clouds and allowing them to collapse faster. As a result, stars began to form more quickly and so did not have the opportunity to accumulate as much mass. So, in this second blush, the quantity of stars forming rose but the mass of each star began to drop.

This cloud, the N11B star-forming region (below), is 160,000 light years away and shows the emergence of a cluster of high-mass stars. The smattering of blue stars on the right of the image exists as some of the largest stars known in the universe today. They each contain more mass than a hundred Suns put together. Clouds like this would have sprung up all over the universe.

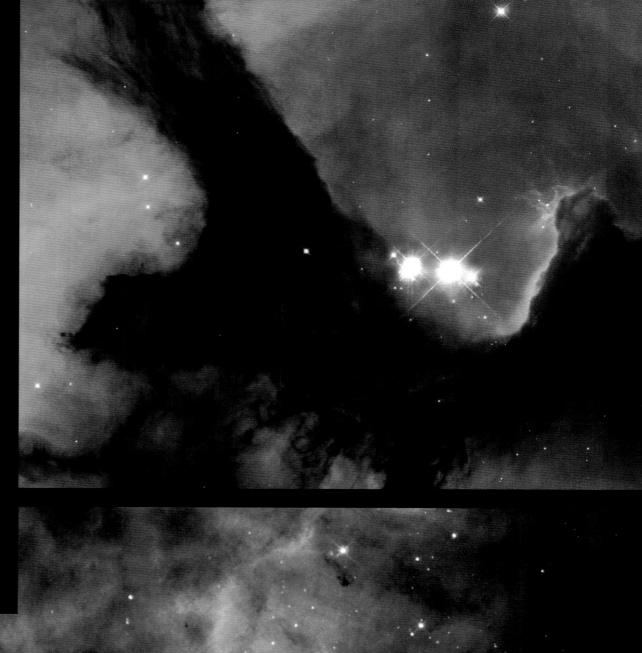

Seeing red in the Trifid Nebula

A million years ago, the Trifid Nebula was a
dark and brooding place. Now it is the Milky
Way's most efficient producer of new stars. At
the centre of the nebula resides a cluster of
massive stars. The combined intensity of their
ultraviolet radiation sweeps through the cloud a
hundred light years wide, forcing the hydrogen
to glow red.

New stars revealed

The tight cluster of blue stars at the top of the
image (below) is composed of relative
newborns in the celestial scheme of things.
Their light illuminates the nearby gas cloud.
In the centre of the image, even newer stars are
about to be revealed from the tip of a glowing
hydrogen pillar.

GIANT STARS

ETA CARINAE

A real megastar

Eta Carinae is the most famous of the
supermassive stars and at 8000 light years, sits
almost on our celestial doorstep. It contains
over a hundred times the mass of the Sun and
is surrounded by a dumbbell of matter that has
been ejected by the star during a giant
eruption. It is one of only a handful of
supermassive stars that have formed recently
in our Milky Way. These stars are extremely
rare and so are highly prized by the
astronomers who find them.

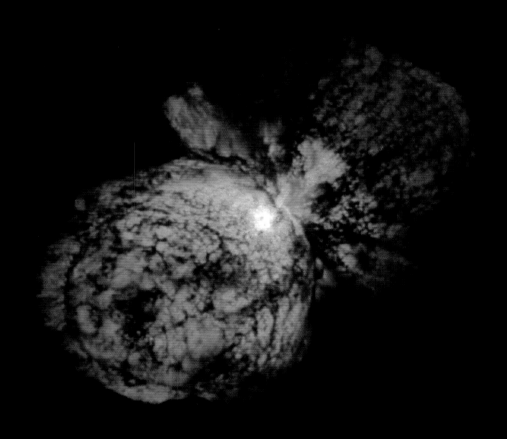

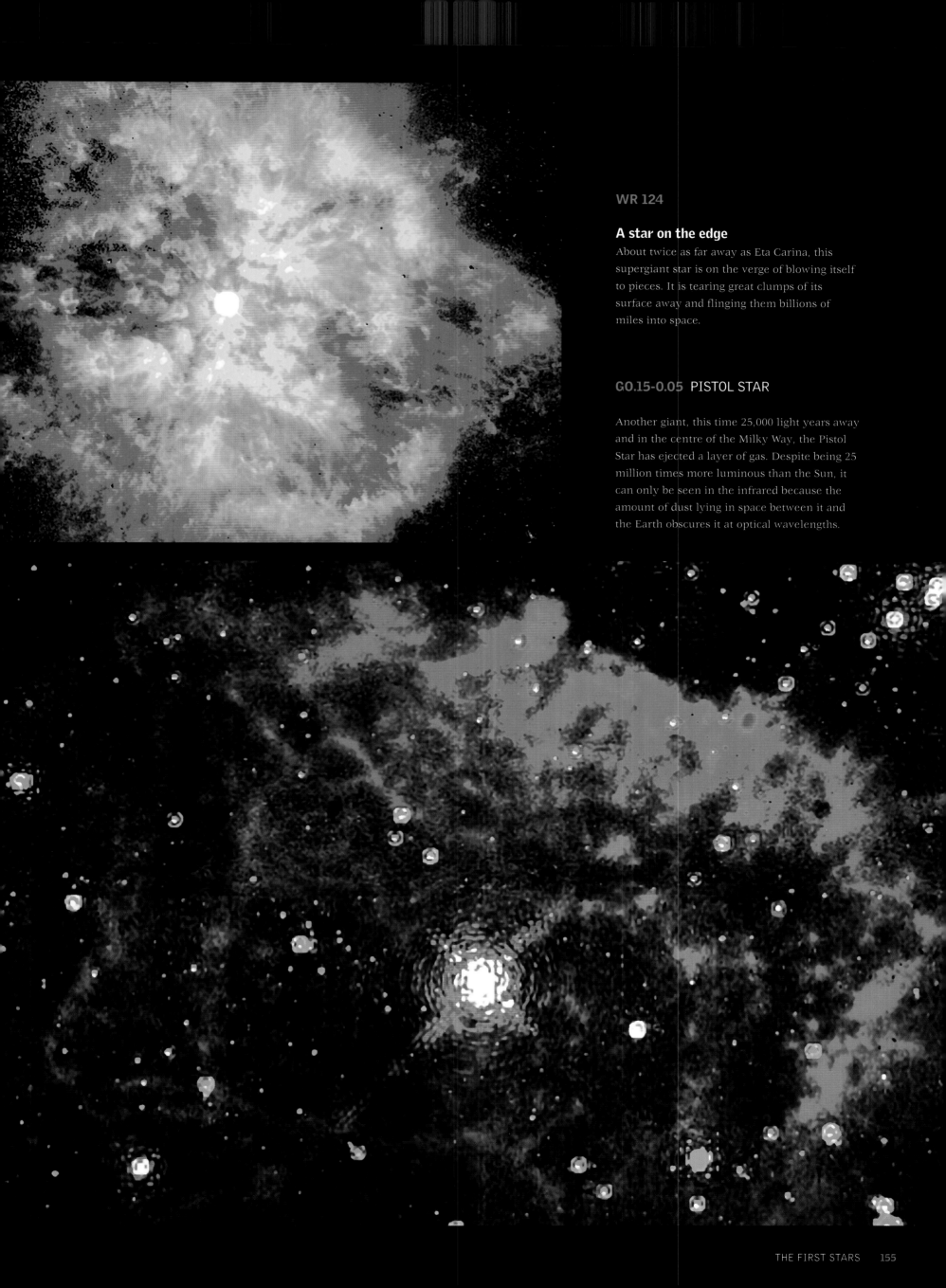

WR 124

A star on the edge

About twice as far away as Eta Carina, this supergiant star is on the verge of blowing itself to pieces. It is tearing great clumps of its surface away and flinging them billions of miles into space.

G0.15-0.05 PISTOL STAR

Another giant, this time 25,000 light years away and in the centre of the Milky Way, the Pistol Star has ejected a layer of gas. Despite being 25 million times more luminous than the Sun, it can only be seen in the infrared because the amount of dust lying in space between it and the Earth obscures it at optical wavelengths.

THE END OF THE
DARK AGES

NGC 3372 CARINA NEBULA

Changing scenery

As the first stars lit up their surroundings, so
the cosmic dark ages came to an end. It must
have transformed the early universe into a
bright place of colourful palettes. Today, we can
gain an impression of what this must have been
like by looking at the surroundings of the
supermassive stars. None better exemplifies
this than Eta Carinae.

Beyond Eta Carinae's immediate nebula,
which is shaped like a dumbbell, a much larger
gas cloud encircles the system. It is the
remains of the molecular cloud that gave birth
to this supergiant and is now being ripped to
shreds by the fury of the central star.

N44C

Stellar cauldron

Just one star appears to be responsible for
the gaseous streamers being blown out of
the nebula shown here (right), but there is a
mystery. The gas seems to be driven faster
than this star can manage. Astronomers
speculate that a hidden black hole may be
helping with the process.

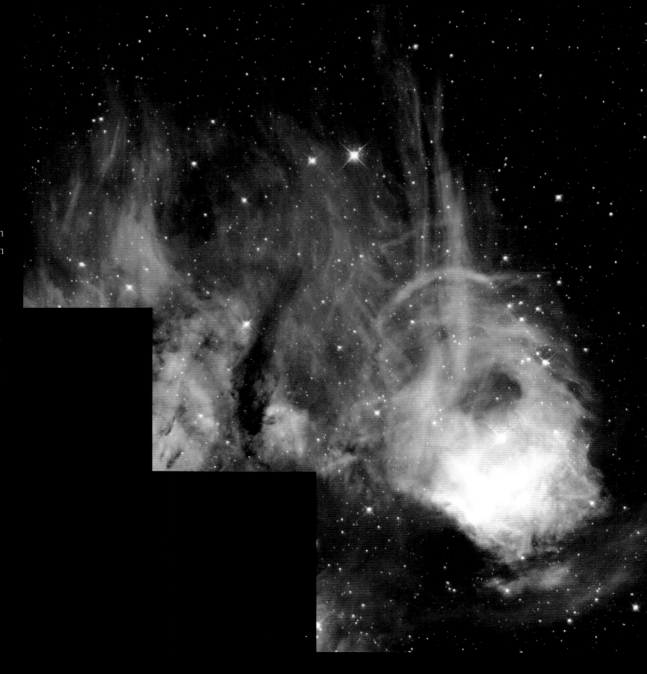

NGC 7635 | BUBBLE NEBULA

Ghostly glow

The Bubble Nebula, NGC 7635, is a shell of
glowing gas, about six light years in diameter,
which surrounds the massive star BD+602522.
It is located in the direction of the constellation
Cassiopeia and was formed when energetic
radiation lifted some of the star's top layers
into space.

THE FIRST STAR CLUSTERS

NGC 346

Brilliant blue stars

As star formation in the early universe began to favour larger quantities of somewhat less massive stars, star clusters must have become bigger and more spectacular. They probably looked quite like NGC 346 in the present-day universe. Over 2500 stars, none of them older than five million years, light up this huge star cluster in the Small Magellanic Cloud, 200,000 light years away. The blue appearance of NGC 346 is a sure sign of interstellar dust. It reflects the starlight of the newborn stars, giving the nebula its characteristic colour.

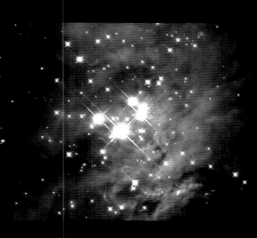

TRAPEZIUM

Nearby giants

The nearest high-mass stars to Earth lie in the centre of the Orion Nebula. The Trapezium stars flared into life around one million years ago and have been lighting this nebula ever since. They are surrounded by a coterie of smaller stars.

HODGE 301

An ageing cluster

Another cluster of massive stars, this time in the Large Magellanic Cloud, Hodge 301 is located 170,000 light years away. Several million years older than NGC 346, some of the largest stars in this cluster have already ended their lives as supernovae. Their explosions have sent shock waves barrelling across the nebula, compressing it into rippling sheets of gas.

ENORMOUS STAR CLUSTERS

R136

Globular cluster in the making?

The largest star-forming region in the nearby universe is known as the Tarantula Nebula. It is in the Large Magellanic Cloud, 170,000 light years away. Were the Tarantula Nebula to be magically transported to the same distance as the Orion Nebula, at just 1500 light years, instead of appearing as a misty 'star' in Orion's word it would be a shining cloud covering the entire constellation.

At the heart of the Tarantula Nebula is the star cluster R136. This image shows the innermost 100 light years of the Tarantula Nebula, containing the star cluster. It is a brilliant collection of nearly 200 high-mass stars. Combined, they total over 2000 solar masses and form such a tight assembly that it has been suggested that they might become a globular star cluster in the future. At present, the stars are each about two million years old.

NGC 1850

Newly minted cluster

When the last curtains of nebulosity have been blown away, stars remain to shine on their own. In NGC 1850, 170,000 light years away in the Large Magellanic Cloud, the most massive stars have now gone, leaving the slightly smaller ones to shine out into space. They are still giants though; each one containing ten times the mass of the Sun.

GLOWING
GAS CLOUDS

IC 434

Glowing veils of gas

The ultraviolet light from massive stars has a profound effect on the hydrogen gas in their surroundings. It strips each atom of its lone electron, by supplying the electron with enough energy to break away from the atomic nucleus to which it is bound. This process is called ionization. When the electron finally falls back into place around a hydrogen atom, it releases its energy, this time as red light.

In IC 434, a veil of ionized hydrogen gas lifts away from the top of a molecular cloud. The ionizing star lies beyond the top of this image. A pillar of dust from the cloud rears up in silhouette over this glowing backdrop, giving this dark cloud its name: the Horsehead Nebula.

N44

Super bubble

The strong wind of radiation and subatomic particles emitted by a collection of massive stars has blown this giant bubble in the hydrogen cloud, NGC 1929. The bubble is known as N44 and is 325 by 250 light years across. It is located in the Large Magellanic Cloud, 170,000 light years away from the Earth. The explosion of a high-mass star at the end of its life also may have helped to carve this gigantic cavity.

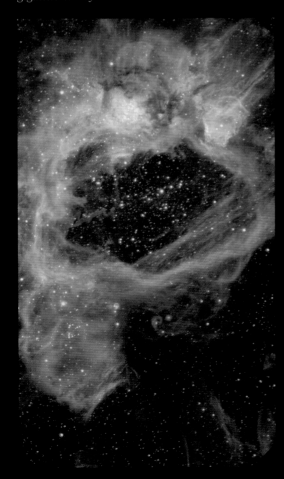

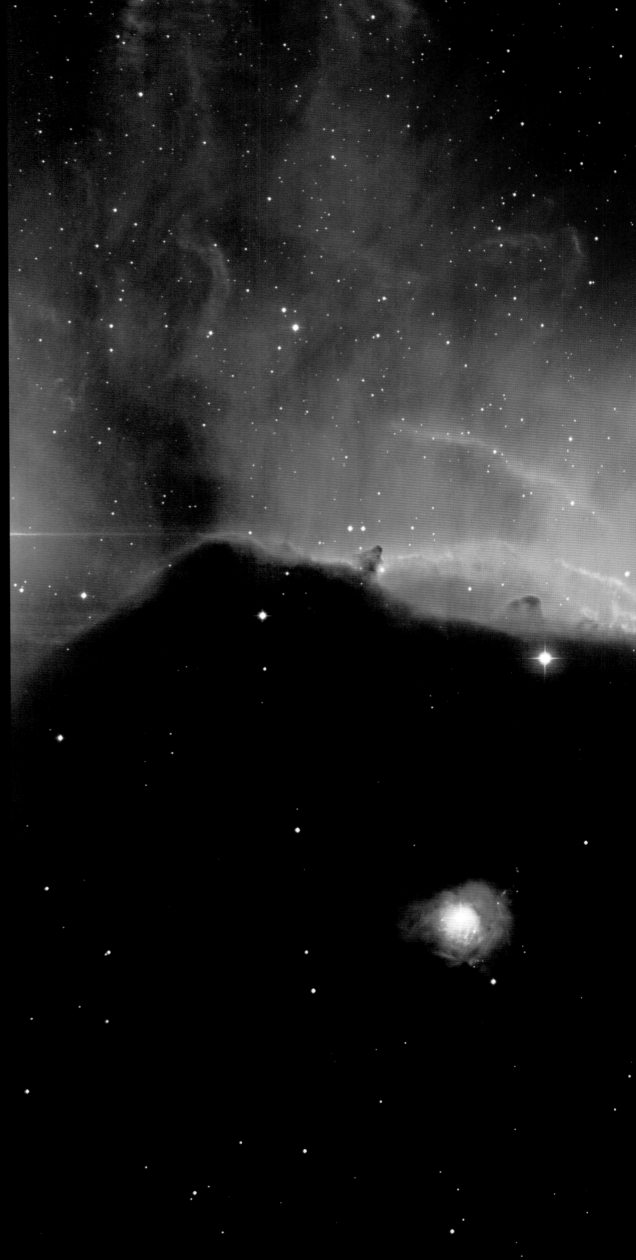

MAKING MORE STARS

THE CARINA NEBULA

Infrared pillars

At infrared wavelengths, we obtain a different view of the star-formation process and the effect that high-mass stars have on their surroundings. It becomes clear that these giant stars are instrumental in helping to build smaller ones.

When a massive star begins to fuse hydrogen into helium in its core, this begins the release of radiation, which energises its surface layers to expel a wind of subatomic particles into space, pushing the surrounding cloud and increasing its density. In turn, this sets off the process of gravitational collapse in pockets of gas within the surrounding cloud, and these fragment and continue collapsing to become smaller stars. Astronomers call these sites of subsequent star formation 'OB associations'. They are named after the massive stars, which are known as type O and type B stars. The O stars are the most massive, containing over 60 times the mass of the Sun. B stars are next with between 18 and 60 times the mass of the Sun.

The pillars that rise in this infrared image hold the stars that have been driven to form by Eta Carina. The light from this monstrous star can just be seen shining down at the top of the image. The optical image of the same region (below) betrays none of the pillar formations.

M8 THE LAGOON NEBULA

The Lagoon Nebula is a large star-forming
factory that sits in the direction of the centre of
the galaxy. It spans some 100 by 40 light years
and lies some 4000 light years away. Under
good conditions during the summer, it can
sometimes be glimpsed by the naked eye, lying
in the deep south of the sky.

W5

Mountains of creation

Around 7000 light years away in the W5 Nebula lie these radiation-hewn mountains of gas. Fashioned by the torrent of ultraviolet light from a nearby massive star, the two most prominent pillars are each 50 light years in height. At their summits, two clusters of young stars are beginning to burst forth and shine their own light into space.

The image has been colour coded so that organic molecules, those made of the life-giving element carbon, show up as red. This clearly illustrates that the two new star clusters have developed in areas rich in the building blocks of Earthly life. Could the planets that are undoubtedly forming around these stars some day harbour life? Only time will tell.

NGC 2264   THE CONE NEBULA

This towering pillar of dust stretches some 7 light years in length and is sited 2,500 light years away. It is doubtlessly the womb inside which dozens of new stars are incubating. The first of these have broken free at the top of the pillar.

image below shows a gigantic star field, one million light years across.

Astronomers have taken this image and painstakingly masked out all of the stars, galaxies and other celestial objects that they can see on it. Next, computer processing boosts the details that were previously extremely faint.

The result is the image below right, which has been colour coded to make the faint light easier to see. The orange tones are the combined light of the first celestial objects. We estimate that this background light emanates from the first billion years of the universe's life.

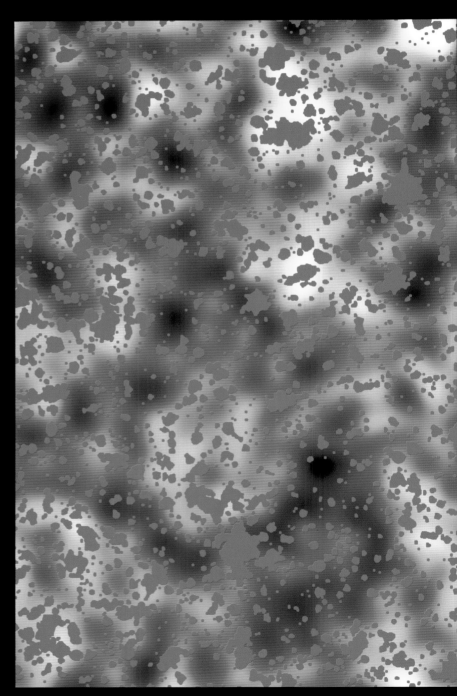

THE FIRST STARS

Out of the darkness

This artist's view shows a web of massive stars in the early universe. Eventually, as telescopes become more powerful, the combined light seen in the infrared image opposite right, will be resolved into individual objects. Then we will be able to tell whether they were correctly imagined.

THE FIRST
STELLAR DEATHS

GRB 990123

A stellar cataclysm

During the late 1960s, a number of satellites sensitive to gamma rays were launched. Their mission was not to look outwards into the universe but to look down towards Earth, scanning for the tell-tale gamma ray blast of secret nuclear weapons tests. Instead, they picked up random bursts of gamma rays coming from somewhere in deep space.

Astronomers now believe that these brief but powerful gamma ray bursts are from the explosions of extremely high-mass stars in the early universe. It may be that the inert core of a hypernova – as astronomers call these super supernovae – may transform directly into a black hole. The gamma rays are then the last 'scream' of the collapsing star before it is swallowed.

At the moment, the gamma ray bursts are the most direct way astronomers have of seeing the first generation of stars.

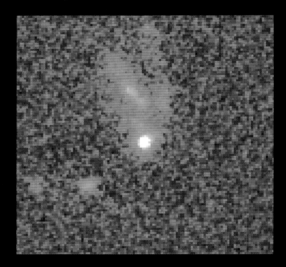

VELA SUPERNOVA REMNANT

Shredded star

The explosion of massive stars in the early universe makes modern stellar explosions look pale by comparison. Even so, today's supernovae are not to be underestimated. These are the shredded remains of a star (right) that blew itself to pieces 11,000 years ago. Situated about 815 light years away, it could probably have been seen in the daytime skies of Earth.

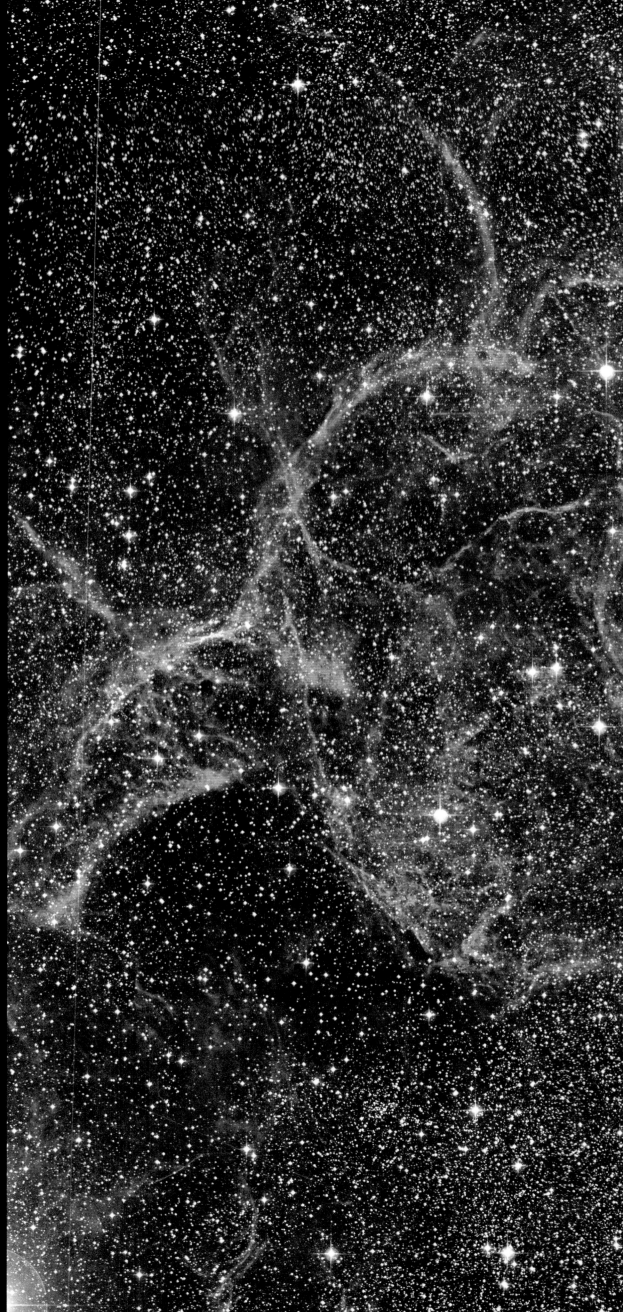

THE FIRST PLANETS

JUPITER

Planetary forefathers

The first planets in the universe were probably great spheres of gas, similar to the gas giant Jupiter in our own Solar System. They were probably larger than Jupiter, however, and can be thought of as halfway between a star and a planet. Such objects still form today and are called brown dwarfs.

We often think of brown dwarfs as failed stars because, even though they contain 15 to 85 times the mass of Jupiter, they still cannot muster the intense pressure and density needed to ignite nuclear fusion in their hearts – the prerequisite to becoming a bona fide star.

Jupiter is made of the same chemicals, in the same proportions, as the Sun. Although it probably has a core of rock and metal containing three-to-five times the mass of the Earth, Jupiter has no solid surface to speak of; the atmosphere simply gets denser and denser the further down it goes.

HD 3651

Brown dwarf discovery

The highlighted star is a nearby brown dwarf. It orbits HD 3651, a star slightly less massive than the Sun that lies just 36 light years away. The brown dwarf's mass is estimated to be between 20 and 60 times greater than Jupiter's.

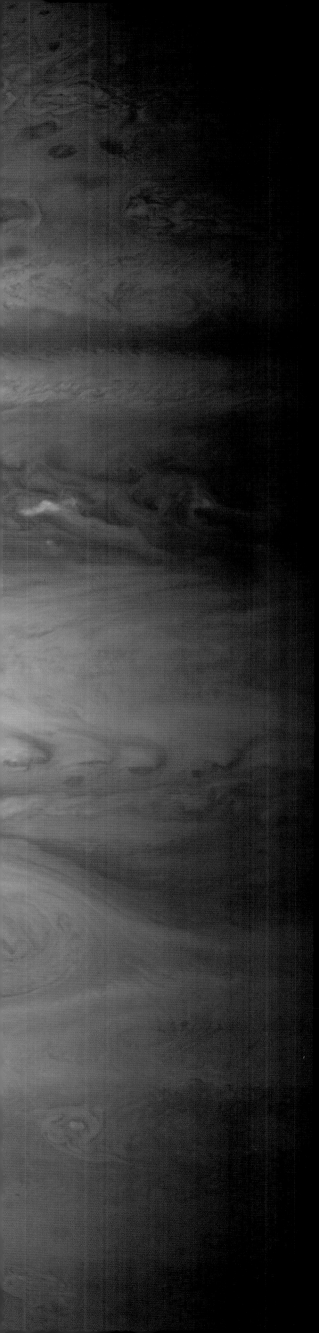

PLANETS OF MANY KINDS

MARS

Rocky planet

As the first stars in the universe died and seeded space with the heavier chemical elements, rocky planets became possible. At around half the diameter of Earth, Mars is a typical rocky world. It is composed predominantly of rocks and metals with a tenuous atmosphere.

URANUS

Ice giant

With a diameter five times the Earth's, Uranus
orbits the Sun 19 times further out than our
planet. It is an ice giant, so-called because it
contains large proportions of water, ammonia
and methane, all frozen into solid particles far
from the warmth of the Sun in the outer solar
system. If an ice giant were to exist in an orbit
similar to Earth's, these ices would melt and
the world might become an ocean planet.

SATURN

Gas giant

Gas giant planets are a second major class of
world. In our solar system, Saturn is ten times
the diameter of the Earth and circles the Sun in
a 29.45-year orbit, ten times further from the
Sun than the Earth. In other planetary systems,
we have found gas giants in much tighter
orbits, whipping around their central stars in a
matter of days.

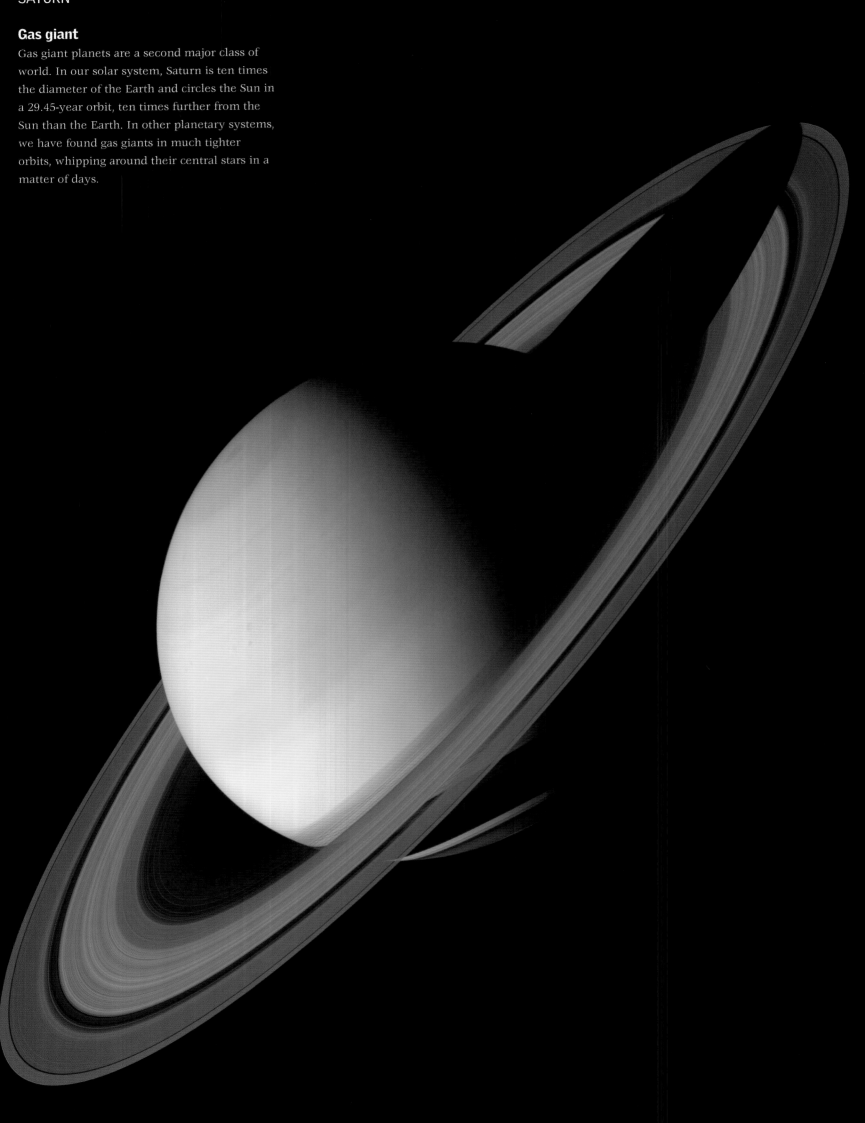

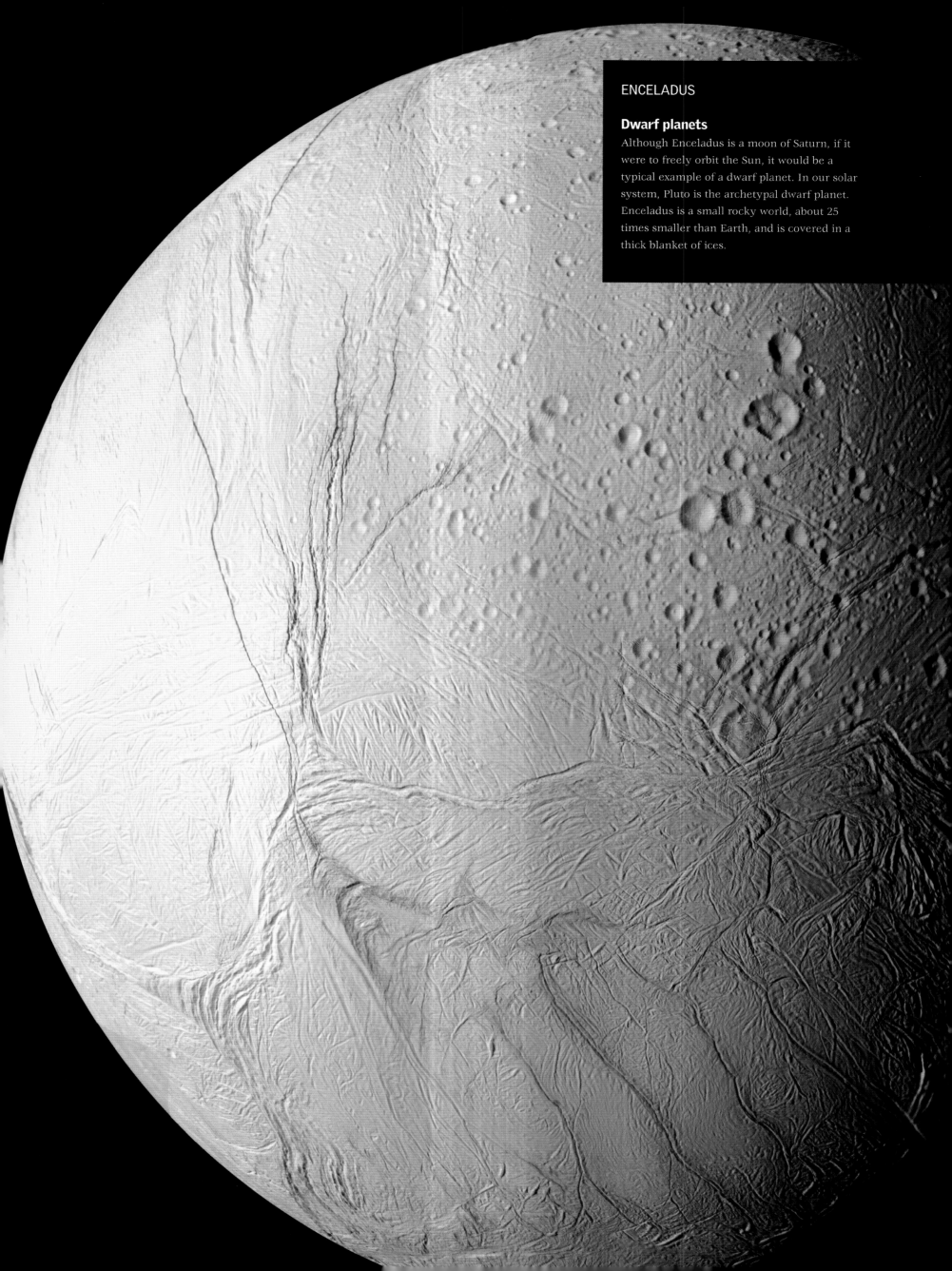

ENCELADUS

Dwarf planets

Although Enceladus is a moon of Saturn, if it were to freely orbit the Sun, it would be a typical example of a dwarf planet. In our solar system, Pluto is the archetypal dwarf planet. Enceladus is a small rocky world, about 25 times smaller than Earth, and is covered in a thick blanket of ices.

EARTH

Are we alone?

In our limited exploration of other planets, Earth remains unique. It is the only world on which we know that life exists. Biologists and planetary scientists are now trying to understand what makes Earth so suitable for life. Undoubtedly, a position fairly near a star is crucial. Earth's distance from the Sun means that we are not too cold, nor too hot, leading some astronomers to call it a 'Goldilocks orbit'.

Biologists are coming to realize that, by breathing, life changes the chemical balance of a planet's atmosphere. Space telescopes are being designed to look for Earth-sized worlds and analyze their atmospheres to tell whether life is present.

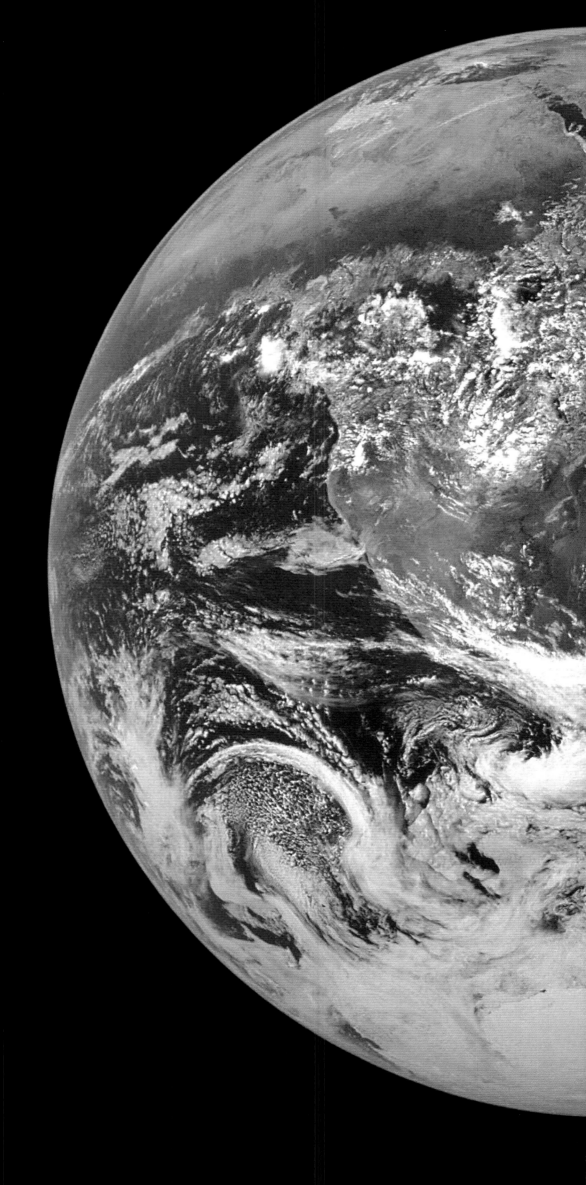

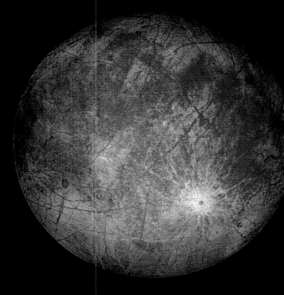

EUROPA

What lies beneath?

Jupiter's moon Europa shows a surface with obvious ice floes. This and other data convince planetary scientists that a global ocean of water lies beneath the icy crust. Could microbes live in this water? Plans are being drawn up to send a spaceprobe to tunnel through the ice and find out.

TITAN

The primeval Earth

Saturn's largest moon Titan may represent the kind of place that Earth was, four billion years ago before life began. The chemistry of Titan is rich in molecules that we believe contributed to the formation of life on Earth. The only reason it did not happen on Titan is because the moon is ten times further from the Sun and so receives little in the way of sunlight to drive chemical reactions.

THE EVOLUTION OF GALAXIES

THE PROCESS OF GALAXY FORMATION AND SUBSEQUENT EVOLUTION TOOK PLACE OVER SUCH AN EXTENDED PERIOD OF TIME AND ACROSS SUCH VAST DISTANCES THAT, DURING THE COURSE OF OUR SHORT HUMAN LIFETIMES, WE SEE THE UNIVERSE AS JUST A FROZEN TABLEAU BEFORE US. THE ONLY WAY WE CAN MAKE SENSE OF IT ALL IS TO USE THE CONCEPT OF LOOK-BACK TIME AND PEER FURTHER AND FURTHER INTO THE PAST. THE LIGHT FROM THESE DISTANT REALMS HAS TAKEN SO LONG TO REACH US THAT IT ALLOWS ASTRONOMERS TO LOOK BACK TO THE WAY THE UNIVERSE USED TO BE.

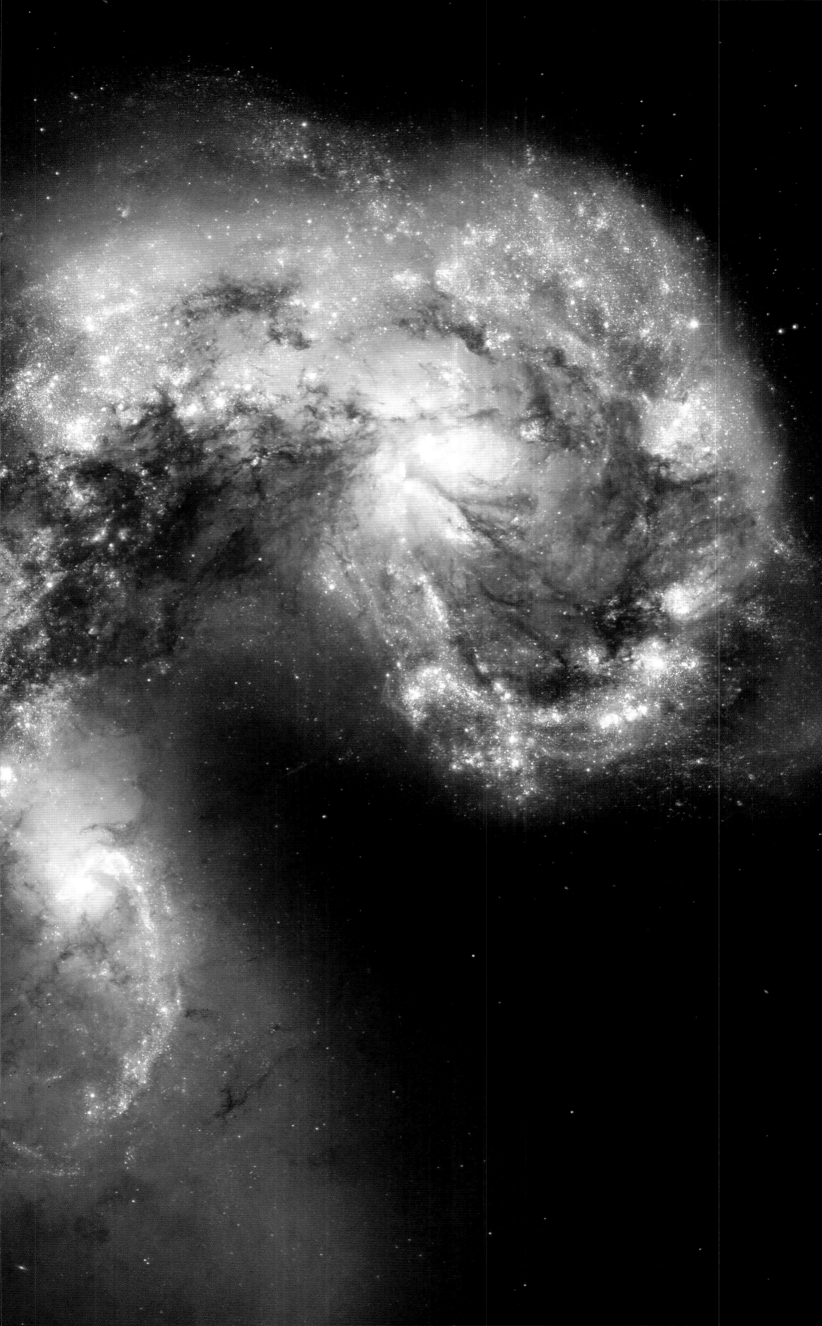

The evolution of galaxies

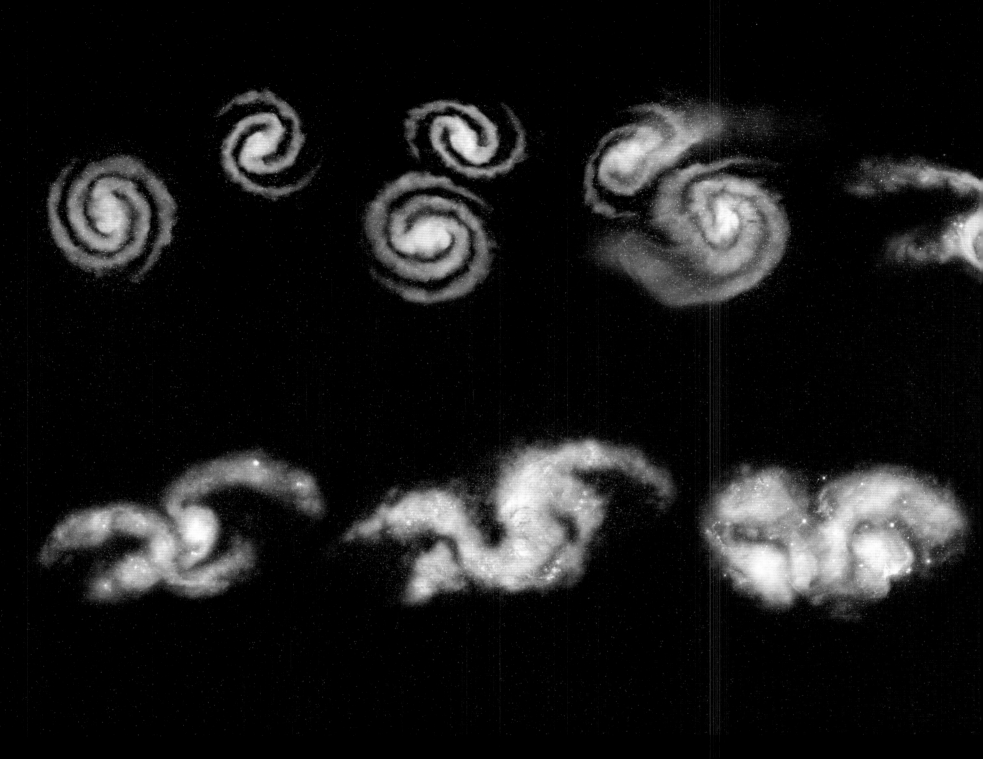

We can therefore see the sizes and styles of galaxy that dominated the universe at earlier times. In this painstaking way, we can build up a picture of cosmic history slice by slice and then interpret what must have happened in between the slices.

Early dwarfs

Using today's foremost telescopes, we can now see back across ten billion years to the first population of galaxies. The images seem to confirm our earlier suspicions that galaxies begin life as dwarf galaxies, consisting of a few million stars or less. These dwarfs then build into larger galaxies by merging together. The path they take, however, is anything but simple.

Once star formation begins, it continues as a self-perpetuating process until there is no more gas left in a galaxy to provide the necessary raw material. Often the triggers to make new stars are the shockwaves rippling through the galaxy from supernova explosions. These compress gas clouds, beginning the gravitational collapse that leads to more stars.

In a dwarf galaxy, however, supernovae can actually stunt the growth because the galaxies are so small that the violent supernova shock waves can expel gas from the galaxy. As the number of supernovae grows, so the majority of the galaxy's gas can be thrown into space. With no more raw ingredients to use, star formation completely stalls and the galaxy's population begins to age, creating what appears to be an old galaxy in a young universe.

The situation is saved when the dwarf galaxies begin to collide with one another and they grow into ever-larger collections of old stars. Eventually, these mid-sized elliptical galaxies build up enough mass to develop appreciable gravitational fields, which begin attracting cool gas from intergalactic space.

While gas heated by supernovae is moving so fast that it continues to escape the galaxy's gravitational grasp, the cooler gas spirals down towards the galaxy and naturally settles into a disc, surrounding it. And as this relatively flat disc accumulates more and more gas, so its density increases and star formation spontaneously begins.

In this way, what was once an elliptical galaxy of old stars is transformed into a spiral galaxy, with its bulge of old stars surrounded by sweeping arms of new stars. The universe's original population of dwarf galaxies therefore

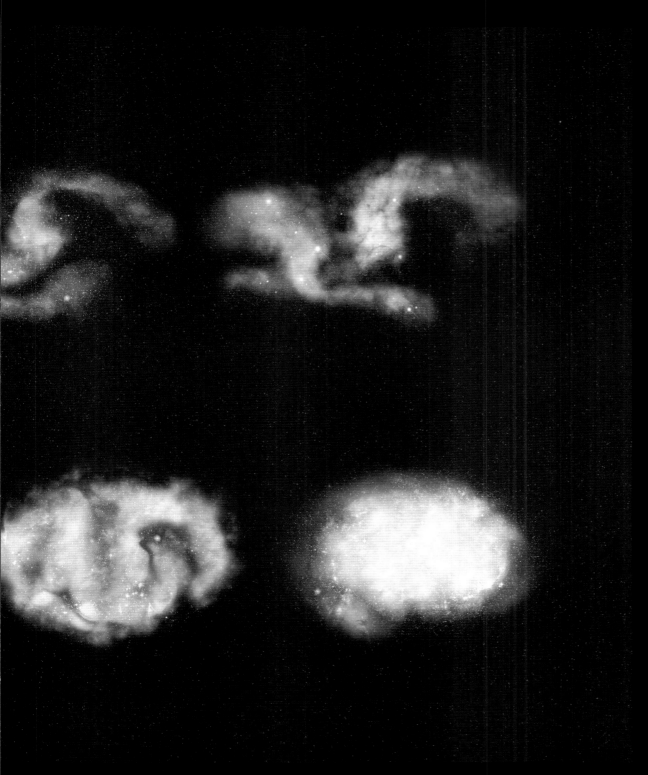

Two spiral galaxies drift into each other's grip and fall together. They usually do not collide head-on but instead circle each other, making a number of closer and closer passes, before finally becoming a single object.

The gravitational force of each galaxy distorts the other, stringing out two tails of stars that mark their pathways to destruction. A typical merger usually takes up to half a billion years to complete. This sequence shows only the initial few encounters. As time passes, the galaxies will continue to swing by one another, edging ever closer, throwing more stars around and becoming messier and messier. Eventually their cores will merge and they will be reborn as a single elliptical galaxy.

become the seeds around which the arms of spiral galaxies form.

Collision time

If these spiral galaxies are left on their own, continually accumulating a gentle stream of gas from their surroundings, perhaps even occasionally cannibalizing a much smaller galaxy, they will retain their spiral shape. However, if they fall within the grasp of a similarly large galaxy and collide, they will have their delicate spiral shapes destroyed.

In the violent collisions, the orbits of each galaxy's stars will be thrown all over, creating a messy elliptical galaxy. Some of the stars and gas will be ejected completely, initially creating discarded tails behind the galaxies which then disperse into intergalactic space.

The collision will force any gas within the galaxies to transform rapidly into stars, triggering a sudden explosion of star formation known as a starburst. In a few hundred million years of creating brilliant star cluster after brilliant star cluster, all of the gas is exhausted. What remains is a large elliptical galaxy.

Although all traces of star formation disappear, in the centre of the merging galaxies there are other dramatic movements afoot. Each galaxy in the collision probably contains a supermassive black hole. As the two most massive objects, they will naturally sink towards the centre of the merged galaxy, where they will inevitably encounter each other. Inexorably they will be drawn into a circling dance of death, forever drawing closer together. As the black holes perform their looping orbits

around each other, their large gravitational fields will sling stars into eccentric orbits, accentuating the elliptical shape of the galaxy.

Eventually, the black holes will meet and merge, releasing a torrent of energy that sweeps through the galaxy as a burst of radiation. The newly enlarged black hole will continue to eat any stray stars, planets or clouds of gas that haplessly wander into its patch. This can be a significant amount of material over the millions of years following a merger because, during this time, the orbits are scattered all over, inevitably placing some unlucky celestial objects on paths that will carry them through the dangerous central regions of the galaxy.

In this violent way, the universe built itself into the apparently sedate place of beauty we see today.

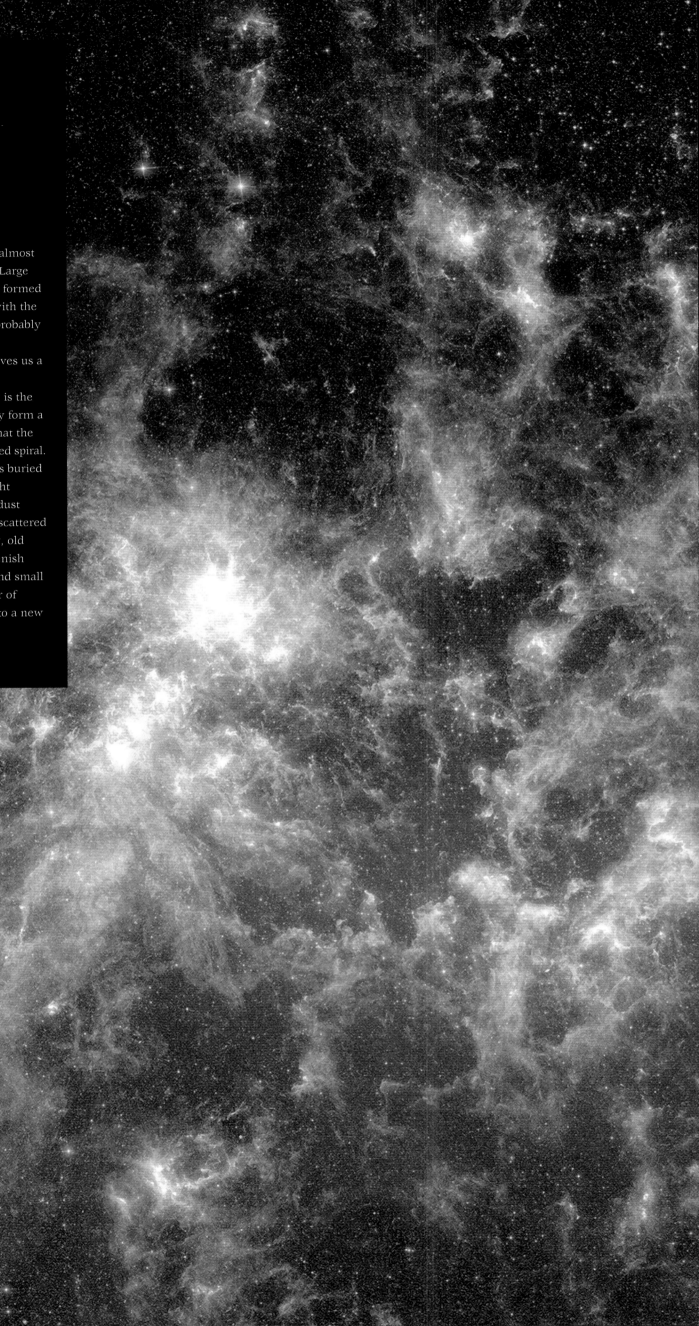

THE FIRST
GALAXIES

THE LARGE MAGELLANIC CLOUD

Beginning with dwarf galaxies

The first galaxies in the universe were almost
certainly dwarf galaxies, similar to the Large
Magellanic Cloud (LMC). These dwarfs formed
the building blocks of larger galaxies, with the
result that every large galaxy today is probably
an amalgamation of many dwarfs.

This colour-coded infrared image gives us a
new way in which to study the stellar
populations in the LMC. The blue glow is the
combined light from mature stars. They form a
central bar across the galaxy, hinting that the
LMC might once have been a small barred spiral.

Beyond the bar, massive young stars buried
in thick blankets of dust excite the bright
chaotic emission. The red wisps show dust
heated by the stars, while the red dots scattered
throughout the picture are either dusty, old
stars or more distant galaxies. The greenish
clouds contain cooler interstellar gas and small
dust grains that are the LMC's reservoir of
material, waiting to be incorporated into a new
generation of stars.

SPECKS IN SPACE

HUBBLE ULTRA DEEP FIELD

Deep discoveries

The furthest galaxies ever glimpsed are shown here, revealing what the universe looked like about a billion years after the big bang. Even by that time, the first dwarf galaxies had formed.

The Hubble Space Telescope captured this image by staring at the same region of apparently empty space continuously for about 1,000,000 seconds, or roughly 11.3 days. During this time, the telescope orbited the Earth 400 times. It revealed 10,000 galaxies within a minuscule region of space, barely one-fiftieth the size of the full moon. By way of comparison, the whole sky is nearly 13 million times larger than the area covered by the Ultra Deep Field.

YOUNG GALAXIES

Galactic building blocks

This series of 36 young galaxies from the Hubble Ultra Deep Field reveals the irregular shapes of these early building blocks. Each galactic 'tadpole' is a small fraction of the size of a modern galaxy.

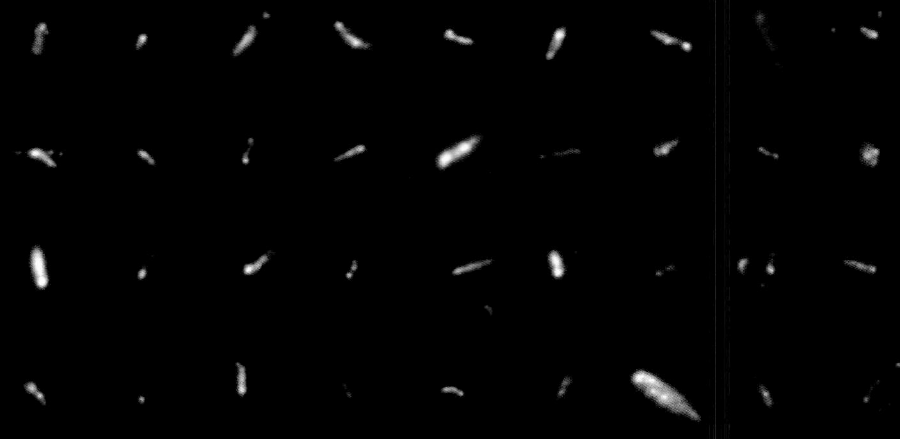

EARLY DWARF GALAXIES

Pushing the red limit

These are the earliest dwarf galaxies astronomers can find in the Hubble Ultra Deep Field. In reality, the stars in them shine blue but the galaxies have been turned red by the expansion of the universe, stretching the light from blue to red. The light from these galaxies has taken around 13 billion years to cross space and reach Earth.

STARBURST
GALAXIES

NGC 4038 & NGC 4039
ANTENNAE GALAXIES

Igniting star formation

One by one, the dwarf galaxies merge with each other. Upon colliding, they rapidly build new stars. Initially these are born in open clusters, which then drift apart and become indistinguishable from the rest of the stars in the galaxy.

The same process but on a larger scale can be seen in the Antennae galaxies. This image has been specially processed to show the starbursting regions in red. Each of these regions is forming a huge star cluster, yet within 10 million years, most of the newly created stars will have dispersed into the mainstream of the merged galaxy. The densest of the star clusters may survive and be thrown out of the resulting galaxy to orbit around it, each becoming a globular cluster.

NGC 1313

Tracing star clusters

A study of nearby starburst galaxy NGC 1313, only 15 million light years away, shows that the disintegration of open star clusters is a relatively rapid process. Astronomers have found short-lived blue stars scattered throughout, apparently at random. This indicates that the clusters in which these stars formed dispersed within about 10 million years – little more than the blink of an eye in celestial terms.

A galactic meal

Once galaxies have become sufficiently large,
they can swallow smaller galaxies without too
much disruption to themselves. Here, the large
spiral NGC 1532 is about to consume the dwarf
NGC 1531. The gravity from the larger galaxy is
beginning to pull the smaller one out of shape
and eventually will tear it apart completely.

Glowing clouds of hydrogen gas show up in
the larger galaxy as red, indicating forming star
clusters, probably induced by the relatively
feeble gravity of the dwarf. A faint spiral arm
is curling upwards from the larger galaxy,
apparently in readiness to embrace the doomed
NGC 1531. This dramatic event is taking place
55 million light years away.

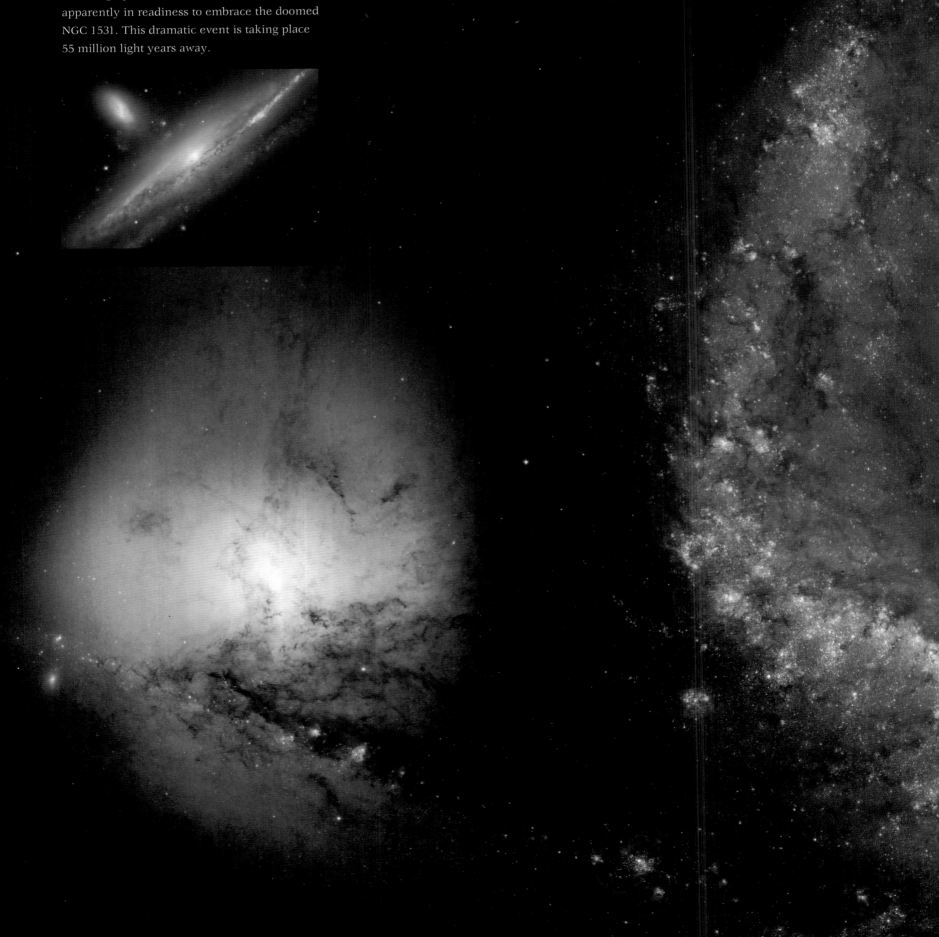

BITE-SIZED MERGERS

M51 & NGC 5195

Preparing food

If we could view NGC 1532 face on, this is what it would probably look like. M51, the Whirlpool Galaxy, is dismembering the smaller galaxy, NGC 5195. In response, vigorous bursts of star formation are lighting up its spiral arms. Eventually, M51 will consume its neighbour but remain relatively unscathed by the encounter.

BULKING UP
A GALAXY

Spider's Web Galaxy

Astronomers have known about a radio galaxy
at this location for years. When we zoomed
in on it visually, using the Hubble Space
Telescope, the reward was our best ever look
at a galaxy in the process of formation.

Resembling a celestial spider's web, this
galaxy is pulling together dozens of dwarf
galaxies to bulk itself up into a bona fide
galaxy. MRC 1138-262 is extremely distant,
located 10.6 billion light years away. The
dwarfs are being sucked into the central galaxy
at speeds of several hundred kilometres or
miles per second, from distances of more than
a hundred thousand light years.

MILKY WAY

Local appetite

The process of bulking up continues in the
modern universe. Using radio telescopes, we
have surveyed the entire sky and detected a
number of gas clouds that are raining down
onto the Milky Way. An inventory of the
composition of one cloud, shown by the oval,
indicates that it has yet to experience much
star formation.

These clouds might be celestial leftovers,
having survived from the era of galaxy
formation billions of years ago. Only now has
the Milky Way's gravity succeeded in snagging
these particular ones. Once inside our galaxy,
the clouds provide the raw materials to help
make new stars.

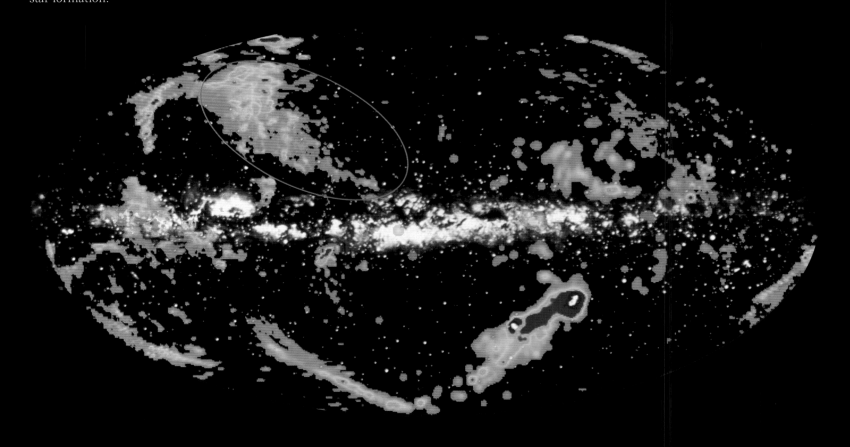

NGC 1427A

Feeling the force

Located 200 million light years away, this irregular galaxy is being dragged into the heart of the Fornax cluster of galaxies. It has been accelerated by the gravity of the cluster to a velocity of 600 kilometres (370 miles per second) and pulled into an irregular shape, some 32,000 light years across.

NGC 6745A

Stretched out spiral

Once a spiral galaxy, NGC 6745A has been distorted by a close encounter with NGC 6745B (not shown in this image). A ribbon of newly minted blue stars points in the direction of the other galaxy.

NGC 4449

Stellar fireworks

Nearly 12.5 million light years away, the dwarf galaxy NGC 4449 blazes with stellar 'fireworks'. Hundreds of thousands of vibrant stars light up the image, having been created by the merging of even smaller 'building block' galaxies. Such 'starbursts' would have been common in the early universe.

GIANT MERGERS

NGC 4676A-B

The Mice

Mergers in today's universe can take place on unprecedented scales. Giant galaxies, each about a 100,000 light years across, fall into each other's deadly gravitational grip and begin to edge towards each other.

Located 300 million light years away, the mice galaxies are heading for such a merger. Their name derives from the tails of stars and gas that each galaxy is leaving behind in space, as they rush towards the head-on collision. The two spirals will eventually slam into one another in 400 million years time, throwing their constituent stars around with a titanic sweep of gravitational forces.

Finally, they will settle and become a single elliptical galaxy.

NGC 1409 & NGC 1410

Merger ahead

A hundred thousand years ago, these two spiral galaxies passed very close; perhaps they even brushed each other. In this near merger, the yellow galaxy NGC 1409 pulled a dark ribbon of material out of its neighbour. Now, 40 billion trillion tonnes of matter a year passes through this intergalactic pipeline and into NGC 1409.

The smaller galaxy shimmers with both the blue of recent star formation and a bright active galactic nucleus, while NGC 1410 remains quiet.

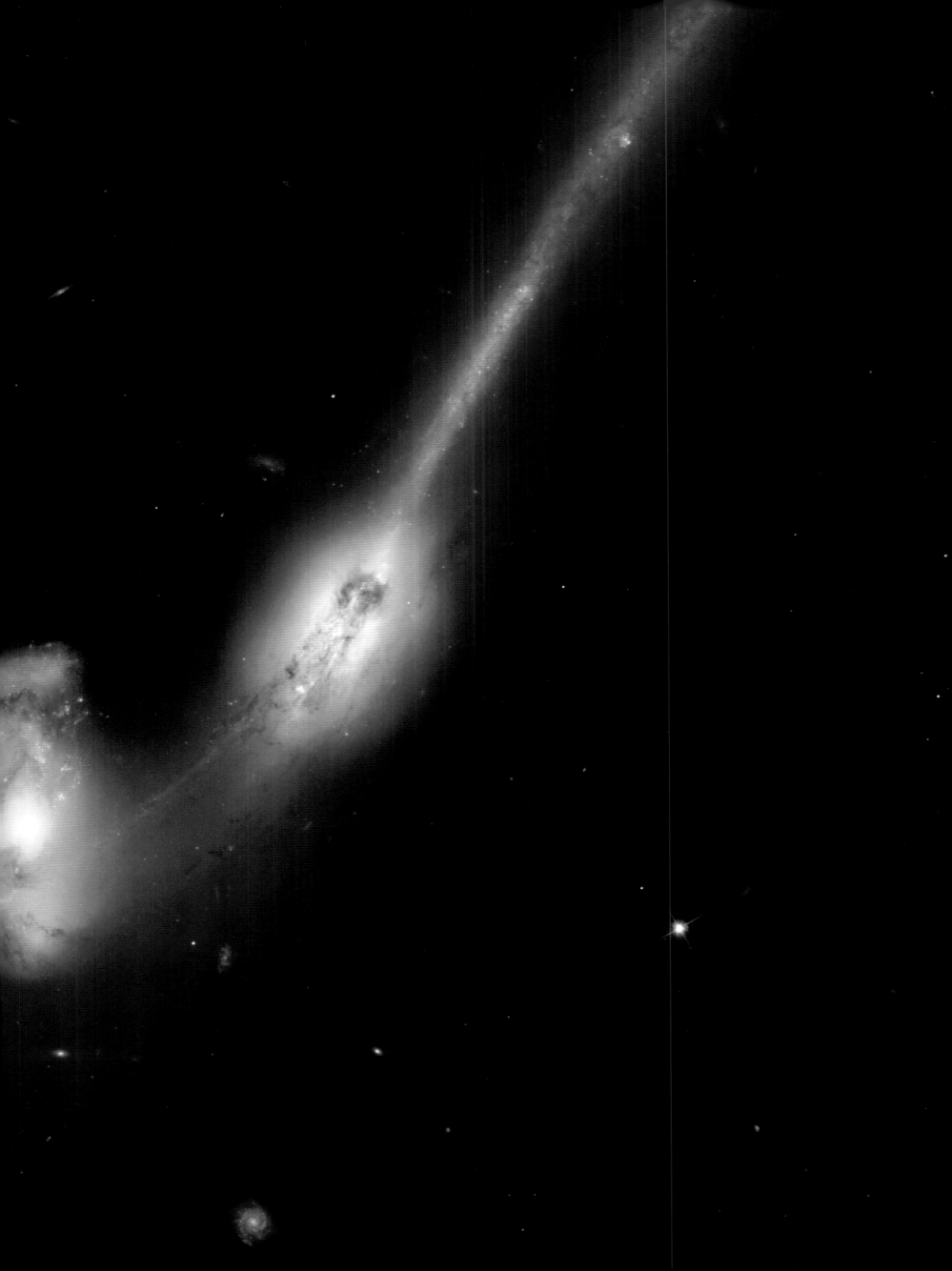

SWALLOWING ITS PREY

UGC 10214 TADPOLE GALAXY

As this galaxy consumes a rival, the only obvious remnant of the unlucky victim is the braided tail of stars and gas. It gives the larger galaxy the appearance of a tadpole and stretches for 300,000 light years across space. Knots of stars in the tidal tail will probably survive and eventually go into orbit around the main galaxy, becoming irregular satellite galaxies, much like the Large Magellanic Cloud around the Milky Way.

The body of consumed galaxy can be glimpsed as the T-shaped enhancement of stars at the upper left of the main spiral galaxy. So the merger is not yet totally complete.

M106

Anomalous arms

Spiral galaxy M106 lies 23.5 million light years away. In optical images, it possesses two beautiful spiral arms, shown here in red. As ever, the arms are dominated by young, bright stars, which light up the gas within. However, in radio and X-ray images, two additional spiral arms pop into view, shown here in blue. These 'anomalous arms' consist mostly of gas. Could they be the result of a merger?

In fact no, they are not. They are jets of matter from a central black hole but, in a unique twist on standard active galaxies, the black hole seems to have fallen over, perhaps having been rocked by a giant merger with another black hole. Instead of the jets squirting out at right angles to the galaxy's disc, they lie almost directly along it.

GALACTIC BULLSEYE

AM 0644-741

Celestial tsunami

If the speed of collision is too great, small galaxies can tear through a larger galaxy like a bullet through paper. A ripple is left behind, as when a stone is dropped into a lake. This ripple works its way out from the point of impact, stimulating star formation wherever it goes. Situated 300 million light years away, galaxy AM 0644-741 is an excellent example of just such a ring galaxy. The sweeping oval of star formation now spans 150,000 light years. Mysteriously, there is no trace of the 'bullet' galaxy.

NGC 4605A

Polar ring galaxy

In certain special cases, one galaxy can strip a passing galaxy of stars and string these around itself to create a ring of stars that circles the galaxy's rotation poles rather than its equator.

These polar ring galaxies are extremely rare. Of the hundreds of millions of galaxies that astronomers have surveyed, only about 100 have been found to display polar rings.

At 130 million light years away, NGC 4605A is the archetypal polar ring galaxy. The yellow galaxy in the centre has somehow encircled itself with a halo of dust and blue stars.

AFTER THE MERGER

An ultra-luminous infrared galaxy

At the relatively nearby distance of around 250 million light years, peculiar galaxy Arp 220 is a prototype for understanding what conditions were like in the early universe when huge galaxies containing supermassive black holes, were colliding together.

Arp 220 collided with another galaxy about 700 million years ago, exciting a frenzy of star birth in a small region about 5000 light years across. It spawned star clusters so compact that they are still bound by gravity. Because of the distance to the galaxy, the clusters show up in the optical image as shining star-like points.

More star clusters must have formed behind the dense clouds of dust in the centre of the galaxy because their light heats the dust and causes it to shine brightly at infrared wavelengths. Astronomers call such galaxies ultra-luminous infrared galaxies (ULIRGs).

By switching to infrared wavelengths, we can see behind the dusty veils. The core is revealed to be a cluster of a billion stars. Its half-moon shape suggests that the bottom half is obscured by an extremely dense cloud of dust about 300 light years across that remains impenetrable, even at infrared wavelengths.

At X-ray wavelengths, astronomers can pinpoint the exact location of the nucleus of one of the colliding galaxies (shown as a blue spot on this image). Another fainter X-ray source nearby (lower right) may be the nucleus of the other galaxy.

Infrared

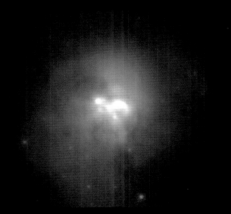

Optical

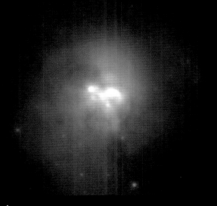

X-ray

Blue straggler stars

In the crowded conditions of a globular cluster, stellar mergers are more common than in the spacious environments found in galaxies. Collisions are responsible for a peculiar type of star called the blue straggler. These are apparently young stars living in old clusters that display no trappings of recent star formation.

When two stars merge, they build a massive star, which can then burn for a short time with a brilliant blue intensity, similar to that of a newly formed high-mass star.

STELLAR MERGERS

The peculiar nova

In January 2002, a star near the outer edges of the Milky Way flared up. At first astronomers thought it was a well-studied type of erupting star, called a nova. However, V838 Mon proved impossible to explain this way when it flared twice more during the next two months. Now, we believe that it was the merger of two stars.

During the first two eruptions, the stars brushed through each other's outer layers. Both near collisions robbed the stars of some more orbital energy, until they finally fell together and became a single object. Astronomers have now monitored the light from the V838 Mon eruptions. It continuously bounces off dust clouds in space, resulting in a celestial bloom, like an opening flower.

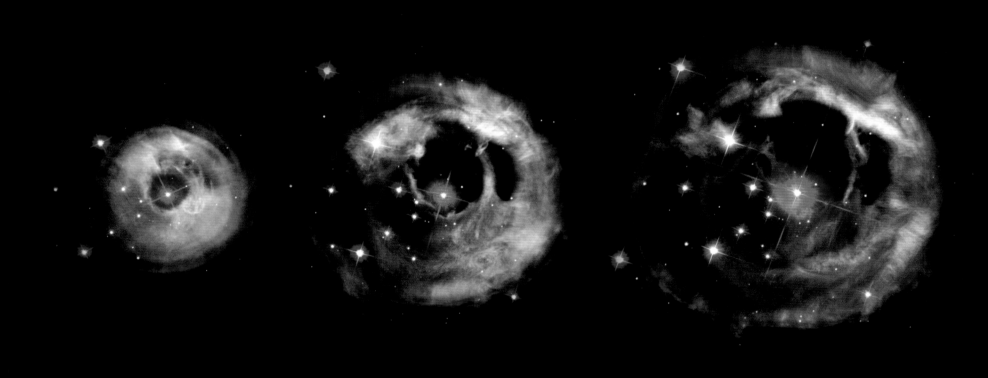

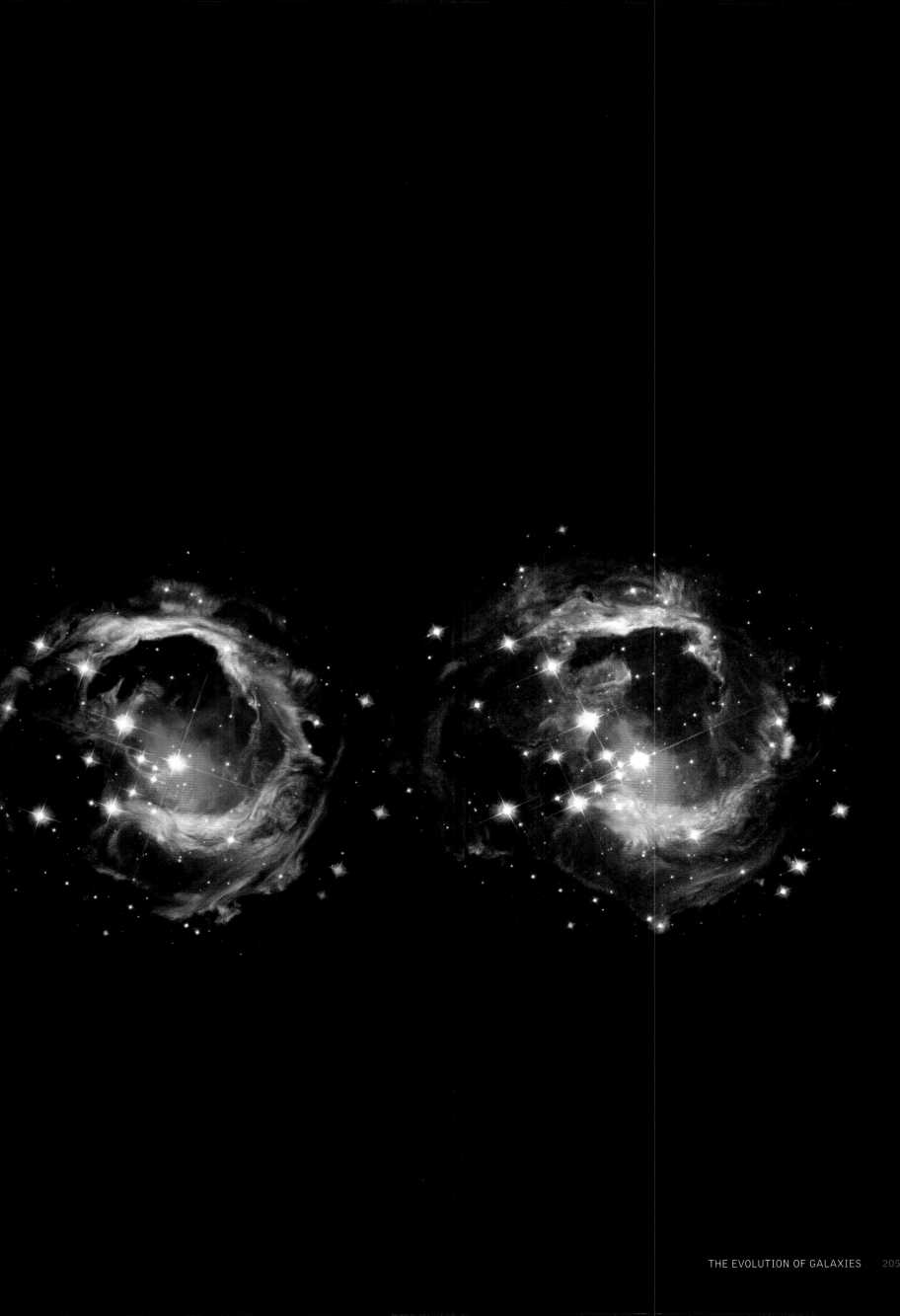

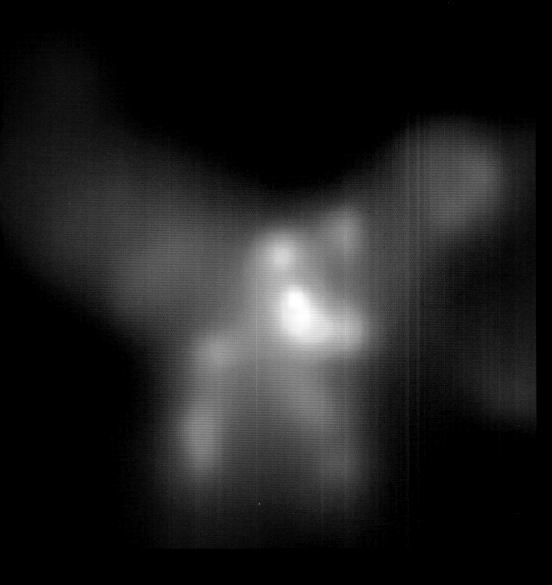

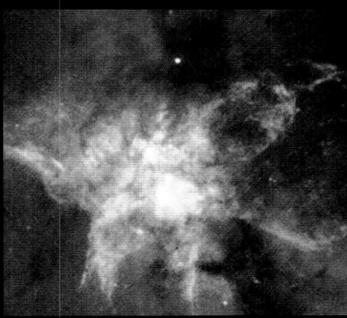

NGC 6240

Messy merger

Some 300 million light years away, NGC 6240 is another merging galaxy heading for a black hole collision. At present the central portions of the galaxy are wreathed in massive starbursts, creating a blinding light at optical wavelengths (above). At X-ray wavelengths (left) the starburst disappears and two monstrous black holes on a collision course are revealed.

The black holes are still 3000 light years apart and the final collision will not take place for a few hundred million years yet.

BLACK HOLE MERGERS

3C75

Celestial Armageddon

This is what an approaching celestial Armageddon looks like. The two bright spots in this X-ray image are supermassive black holes spiralling to a final collision in the heart of radio galaxy 3C75. Both black holes trail jets of particles that reveal their falling motion. Astronomers measure their speed towards each other to be 1200 kilometres per second (750 miles per second), and their separation as 25,000 light years.

When they finally collide, in around three million years' time, they will generate a tremendous explosion of energy, perhaps turning the galaxy into a quasar for a few million years. Thankfully, they are 300 million light years away in the Abell 400 galaxy cluster.

THE COSMIC WEB OF GALAXIES

AT THE SAME TIME AS INDIVIDUAL GALAXIES WERE FORMING, SO THEY WERE BEING DRAWN TOGETHER VIA GRAVITY. INEVITABLY, WITHIN THESE BURGEONING ASSOCIATIONS SOME GALAXIES MERGED BUT MANY SURVIVED AND ALL ARE NOW MEMBERS OF THE VARIOUS GROUPS AND CLUSTERS SEEN THROUGHOUT THE UNIVERSE.

THE FIRST CLUSTER OF GALAXIES WAS RECOGNIZED EVEN BEFORE ASTRONOMERS KNEW WHAT GALAXIES WERE. DURING THE 1780S, CHARLES MESSIER AND HIS ASSOCIATE PIERRE MÉCHAIN DISCOVERED AND CHARTED 16 OF THE GALAXIES IN THE VIRGO CLUSTER, REMARKING ON THE TIGHT GROUPING OF THESE CELESTIAL OBJECTS IN THE SKY.

The cosmic web of galaxies

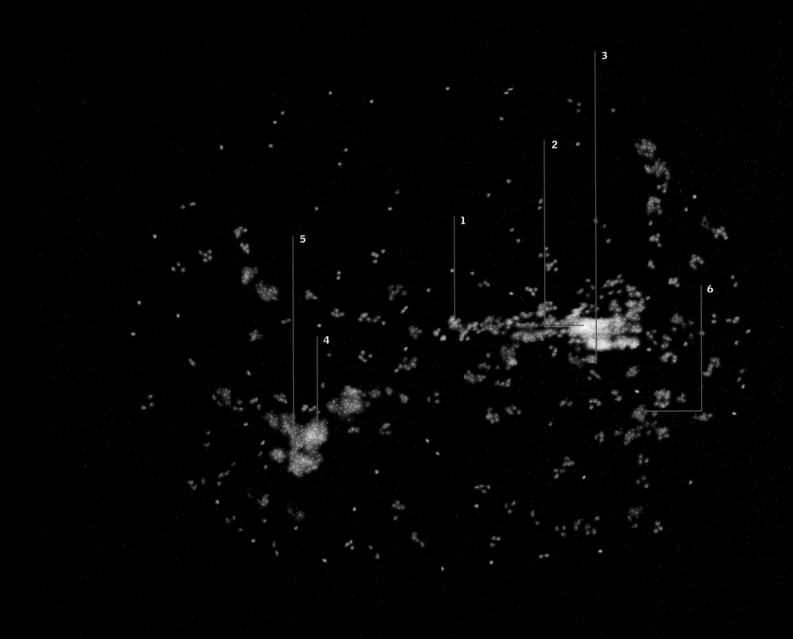

Clusters

Nowadays we know that most galaxies are gravitationally bound to others in such clusters. Our own galaxy is no exception. The Milky Way is just one of 40 or so other galaxies known collectively as the Local Group. Apart from the giant Andromeda Galaxy, most are much smaller, with many of them being dwarf galaxies.

Clusters of galaxies usually contain anything from a hundred to a few thousand galaxies, all of them travelling around a common centre that is often occupied by a massive elliptical. The nearest cluster is Virgo, with some 2000 member galaxies that straggle across the sky. Because of this ragged arrangement, Virgo is an irregular cluster.

Even bigger clusters of galaxies are often more spherical in shape. These can contain many thousands of galaxies, swarming within a region of space no larger than 30 million light years across. The Coma Cluster is a good example of a regular cluster.

In the 1920s, Edwin Hubble put galaxy clusters into their context, by identifying galaxies as external groupings of stars, every bit as grand as the Milky Way. The universe was not just big: it was beyond imagination with respect to the distances between the galaxies and especially from cluster to cluster.

Superclusters

The Local Group and the Virgo Cluster form part of a larger structure dubbed the Local Supercluster. This is a flattened collection of clusters, roughly centred on the Virgo Cluster and incorporating the Local Group on one of its outer edges. The Local Supercluster is actually quite small as superclusters go, spanning 'only' 200 million light years.

Superclusters usually consist of elongated chains of about a dozen clusters, with a combined mass of about ten million billion suns. The Pisces–Perseus supercluster is one of the closest to our own and is much more in keeping with the usual supercluster size. Its backbone can be traced across 300 million light years of the sky.

The superclusters permeate space and contain around 90 percent of known galaxies. Between our own and that of Pisces–Perseus, there is a large patch of emptier space. It is in regions like this where we find the remaining 10 percent of galaxies. Each one is an isolated loner and we call these individuals field galaxies. The large swathes of space they inhabit are termed voids.

Voids can be typically 80 million light years across, although much larger examples are known. The largest void yet observed is in the

12

11

10   7   8

9

Nearby Clusters and Groups

Within 80 million light years of the Local Group, there are numerous groups and clusters of galaxies:

1. Local Group
2. Virgo Cluster
3. Ursa Major group
4. Fornax Cluster
5. Eridanus Cluster
6. Leo II Groups

Nearby Clusters and Voids

Within 200 million light years of the Local Group, the pattern of the nearby clusters of galaxies begin to show the voids as well.

7. Virgo Cluster
8. Corvus Void
9. Puppis Cluster
10. Eridanus and Fonax clusters
11. Pegasus Cluster
12. Delphinus Void

direction of the constellation Boötes. It is colossal with a diameter of about 400 million light years. Taken together, the voids account for around 90 percent of the universe's volume.

Larger-scale structures

We have now surveyed so many galaxies, and identified so many superclusters, that the first hints of an even larger scale structure are beginning to emerge. There is the Great Wall of galaxies. Upon its discovery, during 1989, it became the largest known structure in the universe being some 500 million light years long by 200 million light years wide. It may even be greater still – it is lost from sight behind the Milky Way. Interestingly, it is quite thin at just 15 million light years deep. This vast sheet of galaxies curls around the various voids that lie in this region of space, some 200–300 million light years from Earth.

Astronomers using the Subaru telescope on Mauna Kea, Hawaii, recently discovered a three-dimensional region of space, 12 billion light years away, that extends for 200 million light years in all directions and contains four times the amount of mass that we would expect in such a giant clump. Being so far away, we cannot see the individual galaxies but can spot the gas from which the galaxies are forming.

The gravity from the various clusters and superclusters of galaxies resists the expansion of the universe. Within clusters and groups, the gravity generated by the individual galaxies is enough to completely overcome the tendency to expand, so these galaxies will always remain bound together.

However, the superclusters are insufficiently dense to completely resist and so are forever stretched by the expanding universe, elongating them still further. With very little

matter to provide any gravity, the voids suffer the full expansion rate of the universe.

Then there is the Great Attractor (see Chapter 3). Astronomers cannot even see this mysterious object because it lies behind the Milky Way. However, they are certain it is there because it seems to be dragging everything towards it. Deviations from the smooth Hubble expansion of the universe reveal motion due to gravity and, when astronomers chart these 'peculiar motions' as they are called, of nearby galaxies and clusters, they all seem to be pointing in the same direction. All galaxies out to 200 million light years appear to be affected. Our own is moving towards it at a speed of 600 kilometres per second (400 miles per second). Calculations show that the Great Attractor, which is probably a huge mass of galaxies, must contain 50 thousand trillion solar masses and be 145 million light years away, behind the Milky Way.

THE LOCAL
GROUP

M33

The Milky Way's smaller sibling

Also known as the Triangulum Galaxy, after
the constellation in which it appears, M33 is
the third spiral in the Local Group of galaxies.
At just over half the size of the Milky Way, it is
representative of the typical size of most spirals
in the universe.

M33's distance from the Milky Way is 2.9
million light years, in the same direction as,
and putting it close to, the other giant spiral
in the Local Group, the Andromeda Galaxy.
So close, in fact, that M33 is probably in a
long orbit around Andromeda.

NGC 604

Furious star formation

The Triangulum Galaxy may be small compared to the Milky Way but it contains a star formation region that dwarfs anything in our, or any other, galaxy in the Local Group. NGC 604 spans 1300 light years and contains thousands of new stars, at least 200 of which are giants, some of them over 100 times the mass of the Sun.

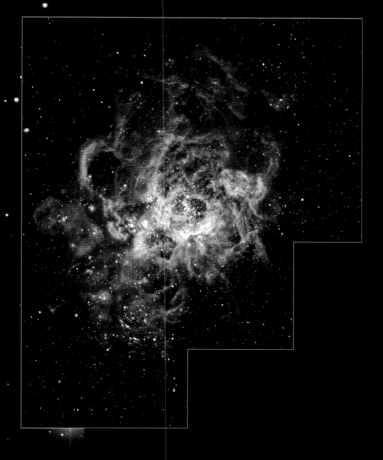

NGC 6822

Barnard's Galaxy

A less assuming member of the Local Group, Barnard's Galaxy is one of the dwarf irregulars that dot our family of galaxies. It sits 1.8 million light years away and spans 10,000 light years in diameter.

The giant galactic hub

The elliptical galaxy ESO 325-G004 presides
over a group of galaxies, called Abell S0740.
With a membership of 100 billion stars, it
contains roughly half the number of the
Milky Way. However, it has globular clusters
in abundance. There are thousands of them
surrounding this galaxy whereas the Milky
Way possesses just over 150.

There is at least one large spiral in the
group, shown bottom right, and dozens of
smaller galaxies dot the image. The distance
to Abell S0740 is 463 million light years.

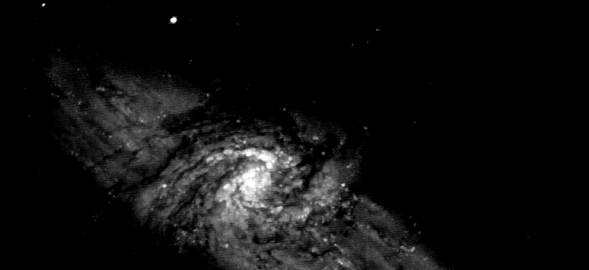

Celestial illusion

Not all galaxy groups are to be believed.
Here, one galaxy slides in front of the other,
separated by tens of millions of light years.
NGC 3314a, the nearer of the two, is 117 million
light years away, whilst NGC 3314b lies at 140
million light years.

GROUPS OF GALAXIES

NGC 6027 & 6027A–E

Seyfert's Sextet

Six small galaxies, apparently all crowded
together, Seyfert's Sextet is squeezed into a
volume of space equal to the diameter of the
Milky Way. As expected from such a tight
grouping, gravitational interactions are afoot.
One of the lower galaxies is being pulled apart
by the gravity of the others. Its stars are trailing
out to the right of the image.

When Carl Seyfert first discovered this
group and published details in 1951, he could
not see the fainter middle section of this tidal
tail and classified it as a separate galaxy.
So should Seyfert's Sextet really be Seyfert's
Quintet? The bad news does not stop there.

One of these galaxies is an impostor. The
group lies 190 light years away but the face-on
spiral galaxy in the centre actually resides five
times further away. Only by chance alignment,
does it appear in the gap between the other
galaxies. So, this is really Seyfert's Quartet.

The four galaxies are destined to merge into
a single elliptical galaxy.

CLUSTERS
OF GALAXIES

Abell 2667

One cluster's Comet Galaxy

Galaxy cluster Abell 2667, situated 3.2 billion light years from Earth, contains hundreds of galaxies and some of the hottest gas known to exist in a galaxy cluster. X-ray observations show that the rarefied gas distributed outside the galaxies, throughout the cluster, is at a seething 10–100 million degrees Celsius. Astronomers thought that such 'intracluster gas' was somehow stripped out of the individual galaxies; now we have proof.

In the upper left of this image is the so-called Comet Galaxy. It is a spiral galaxy that is trailing stars and streamers of gas behind it, rather like a comet trails dust and gas as it sweeps through the solar system. In the case of the galaxy, it is speeding through the cluster at a measured 1000 kilometres per second (600 miles per second). It has been accelerated by the combined mass of the other galaxies and, travelling through the rarefied gas at this speed, the galaxy drags the gas out behind it, igniting star formation in the trailing streams.

Careful analysis of the image shows that there is a faint light throughout this cluster. Astronomers believe it is the pale glow from billions of orphaned stars, all of them ripped from their parent galaxies by the pressure of the intracluster gas.

COMA CLUSTER

Infrared reveals dwarf galaxies

The green smudges on this image are faint dwarf galaxies in the Coma Cluster, 320 million light years away. Galaxies that can be seen at visible wavelengths are colour-coded blue, while the infrared discoveries are shown in red and green. The infrared observations show that there are thousands of dwarf galaxies in the Coma Cluster.

THE NEAREST CLUSTER
OF GALAXIES

M87

M84

M86

VIRGO CLUSTER

The giant next door

The Virgo Cluster dominates our celestial neighbourhood. It contains 2000 galaxies bound together by gravity and, even though it is 60 million light years away, it still has an effect on us. The combined force of gravity is so large that it is pulling both the Milky Way and the other galaxies in the Local Group in Virgo's direction.

We are in no danger of colliding, however, because the expanding universe is driving the Virgo Cluster away from us at 1100 kilometres per second (700 miles per second). So as time goes by, the gravity of the Virgo Cluster will progressively loosen its grip on us.

At the heart of the cluster is the giant elliptical radio galaxy, M87. X-ray observations of the Virgo Cluster show that most of the high-temperature gas within it is centred on M87, in a cloud that spreads across a volume about one million light-years in diameter.

M87 then forms a chain with other bright galaxies that are strung through the cluster, notably M84 and M86. A halo of X-ray emitting gas gives M86 a comet-like appearance and indicates that it is falling towards the centre of the cluster with a velocity of 1500 kilometres per second (900 miles per second), almost certainly on a collision course with M87.

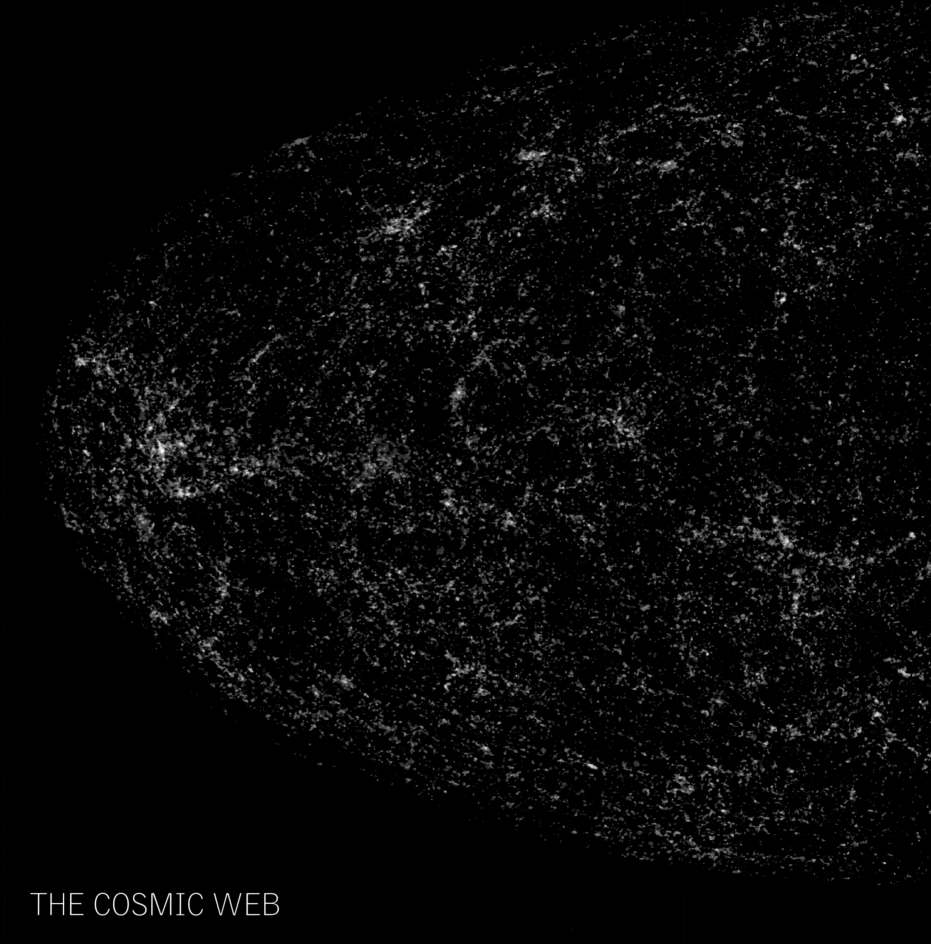

THE COSMIC WEB

2MASS

Galactic survey

This is the finest map of galaxies in the nearby universe. It collects together 1.6 million of them from within a radius of 380 million light years and plots their position on a map of the sky. It is based upon an infrared survey of the entire heavens called 2MASS, short for the 2 Micron All-Sky Survey. The different colours represent approximate distances to the galaxies with the blue ones being closest to us and the red ones furthest away.

The map reveals that galaxies are not scattered at random throughout the universe. Instead, about one-half club together in groups and clusters while the rest are strung through the universe in long chains and filaments that constitute the cosmic web. The groups and clusters form intersections in these filaments.

Because of this arrangement we also see the voids, those areas of space that are largely empty of galaxies. They are similar to the holes in a natural sponge or the space in the middle of foam bubbles. Referring to this analogy, astronomers sometimes describe the universe as having a foamy structure.

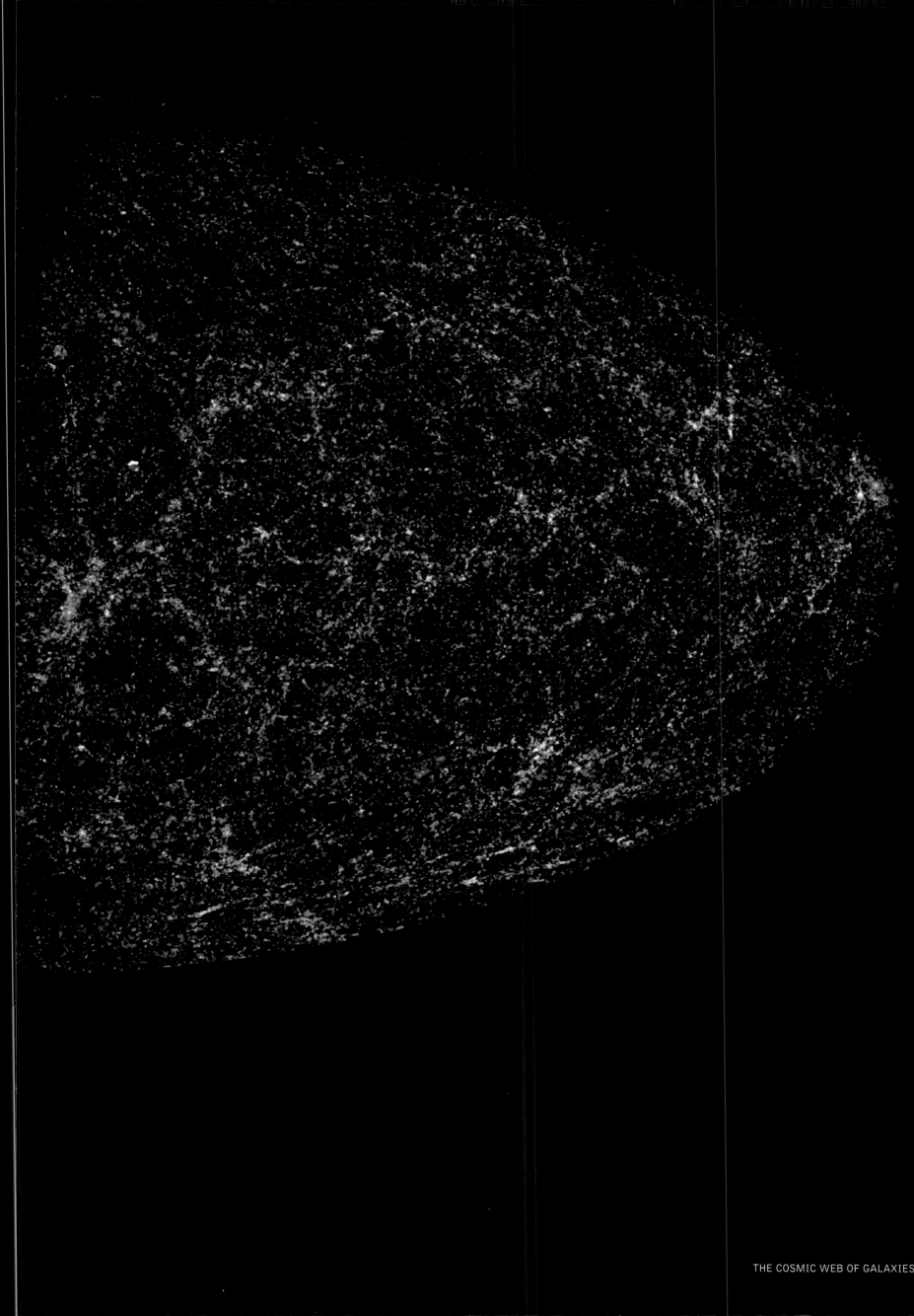

THE COSMIC WEB OF GALAXIES

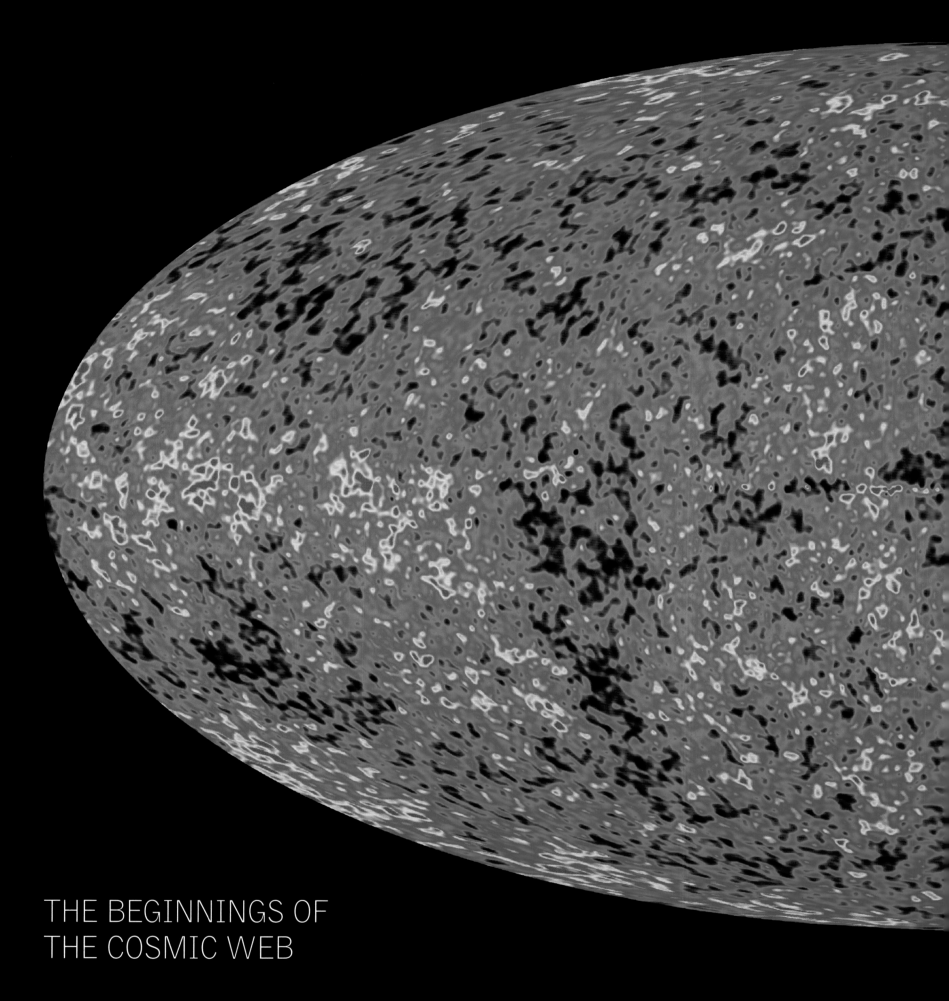

THE BEGINNINGS OF
THE COSMIC WEB

THE COSMIC MICROWAVE
BACKGROUND RADIATION

Before stars and galaxies

A survey of the entire sky at microwave wavelengths reveals a patchwork of exquisitely subtle ripples, caused by equally subtle variations in the density of gas across the universe just 300,000 years after the big bang. At this point in cosmic history, there were no stars or galaxies, just a vast universal ocean of gas in the process of fragmenting to form the first celestial objects. The small variations in the density of the gas can thus be thought of as the seeds of modern large-scale structure in the universe.

The ripples in the microwave background show temperature differences of between 0.005 to 0.0002 degrees Celsius. The cooler regions were denser than the hotter regions and so would have succumbed faster to the pull of gravity. These are today's clusters of galaxies, whereas the hotter regions would become the voids.

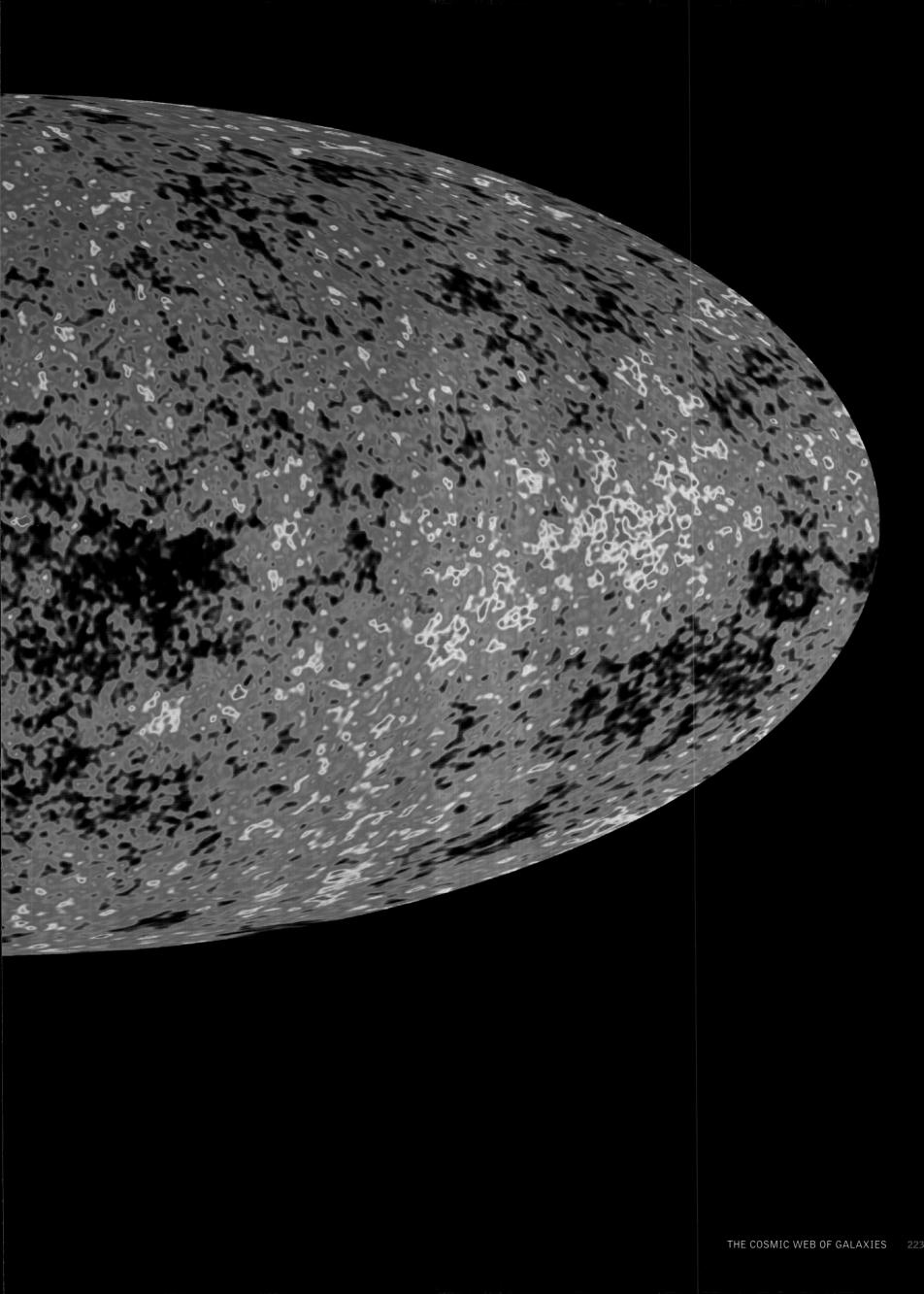

THE DARK UNIVERSE

WHILE STUDYING THE GALAXIES AND THE WAY THEY MOVED, WE BECAME AWARE OF A PUZZLE. GALAXIES WERE ROTATING SO FAST THAT BY ALL CALCULATIONS THEY SHOULD TEAR THEMSELVES APART.

ASTRONOMERS REACHED THIS CONCLUSION AFTER WORKING OUT THE AMOUNT OF MASS INSIDE A GALAXY FROM THE AMOUNT OF VISIBLE STARS. FROM THESE ESTIMATES, THE GRAVITATIONAL FIELDS COULD BE CALCULATED AND IT BECAME CLEAR THAT STARS IN THE OUTER REACHES OF A GALAXY WERE TRAVELLING FASTER THAN GRAVITY COULD HANG ONTO THEM. YET GALAXIES WERE NOT GETTING SMALLER; NONE WAS EXPELLING STARS UNLESS IT WAS INVOLVED IN A MERGER WITH ANOTHER GALAXY. SO HOW COULD THEY REMAIN STABLE?

The dark universe

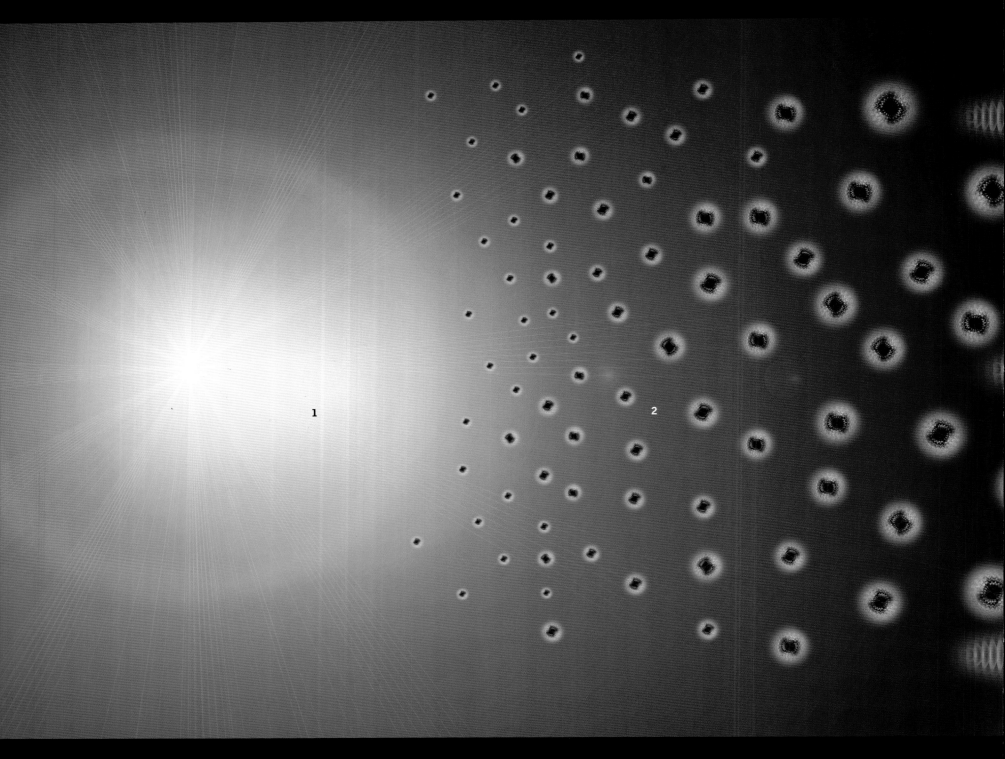

1

2

The missing mass

Generous quantities of matter in the form of gas and dust clouds, black holes and even planets were added to the calculations in an effort to beef up a galaxy's gravitational field, but this still failed to explain how each galaxy retained its shape. It was as if there was even more missing matter, probably ten times more, that needed to be accounted for.

In clusters of galaxies, there was a similar 'missing mass' problem – they did not seem to contain enough matter to hold onto their constituent galaxies. But as with galaxies, there was no sign of the clusters dispersing. Astronomers became convinced that there were no large quantities of normal matter waiting to be found. Whatever this missing material was, it did not react with light at all – otherwise we would have seen its

silhouette. It must only communicate with the rest of the universe through gravity, but what was this dark matter?

By the 1970s, particle physicists had a number of suggestions. Attempting to explain all of the matter and forces in the universe in terms of subatomic particles, they needed to invent certain particles to act as building blocks for others, or to carry forces across the universe. It seemed likely that these particles were the dark matter that astronomers sought.

As cosmologists began to run computer simulations of galaxy formation, they too came across a problem. It seemed that gravity was not strong enough to pull normal matter together fast enough to create the galaxies seen in the universe. Dark matter might provide a solution to this problem, too, causing the extra

gravitational pull necessary to speed up the process of galaxy formation.

Astronomers and particle physicists have been searching for dark matter ever since. However, particle accelerators have not created dark matter and computer simulations of it in astronomical and cosmological situations often seem contradictory. In response, a number of physicists are now wondering whether dark matter really exists at all. Perhaps, they suggest, instead of missing mass, the problem is too much gravity.

If this were the case, it would mean that Einstein's description of gravity was not accurate over extremely large cosmic distances. On such scales, gravity would not act in quite the same way as it does within the solar system. Fledgling theories of modified gravity do exist and some of them even look more

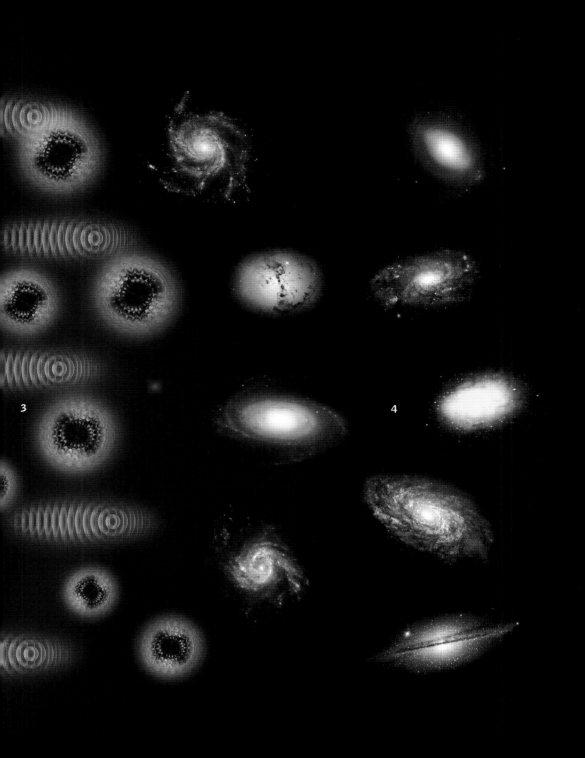

3

4

Building galaxies using dark matter

Step 1: Following the big bang, the amount of radiation in the universe is so dense that it constantly collides with particles of normal matter. These collisions prevent gravity from building the normal matter into clumps.

Step 2: The dark matter does not interact with radiation and so, as soon as it is created, it can begin to collapse together into clumps.

Step 3: When the expansion of the universe has sufficiently diluted the radiation, collisions between it and normal matter all but stop. This watershed in cosmic history takes place 300,000 years after the big bang. The release of the cosmic microwave background radiation corresponds to this moment. Freed from the bullying grip of the radiation, normal matter can begin to clump together through gravity.

Step 4: The clumpy dark matter provides gravitational traps into which the normal matter naturally falls. It speeds up the process of galaxy formation and means that the dark matter provides the skeleton of large-scale structure in the universe.

promising than dark matter as a means of explaining the rotation of galaxies.

Astronomers, cosmologists and physicists continue to debate the merits of dark matter vs modified gravity vigorously, as they maintain their efforts to understand the rotation of individual galaxies and the orbital speeds of galaxies in clusters.

Anti-gravity

In 1998, something happened that changed our view of the universe completely. Two teams of astronomers, each working independently, discovered that the expansion of the universe was speeding up. This went completely against their expectations. We had always assumed that the combined gravity of all the celestial objects would resist the expansion of the universe and gradually slow it down. Instead, the

accelerating universe will continue to drive the expansion of space faster and faster.

This is a mystery for astronomers, cosmologists and physicists to solve. It seems to prove that an extra 'something' is present in the universe. Labelled 'dark energy', it is subtle but strong and capable of overwhelming the combined gravity of everything – yet there is no natural explanation for it anywhere in current physics.

There is, however, a term buried in general relativity, called the cosmological constant that may point us to a solution. It dates from Einstein's early version of the theory when he, like many of the time, believed that the universe was static. His equations predicted an expanding or contracting universe and so he used mathematics to introduce a term in his equations that provided an anti-gravity force. He called

this the cosmological constant and fine-tuned it so that it provided just enough repulsion to counteract the attractive force of gravity.

When Edwin Hubble showed that the universe was indeed expanding, Einstein called the cosmological constant his 'biggest mistake'. Now, modern astronomers are reviving it. If it were a little stronger than Einstein's version, it could make the universe accelerate.

However, the cosmological constant is inconsistent with modern theories of particle physics. So which is wrong? Understanding dark energy and dark matter provides the modern focus for cosmologists in their attempts to comprehend the workings of the universe.

MORE THAN
MEETS THE EYE

NGC 5866

Measuring the rotation of a galaxy

Astronomers measure the rotation rate of a galaxy using the Doppler effect, which relates movement to a shift in the wavelength of light. The best galaxies to use for these measurements are the edge-on spirals, such as NGC 5866, because one side of the galaxy rotates away from us while the other swings towards us. The side moving away has its light rays stretched, while on the other side the rays are squashed. This is not obvious on ordinary images, but special analysis techniques that isolate single frequencies of light reveal the effect.

By studying many galaxies, we now believe that the majority of galaxies rotate too fast, considering how much mass they appear to contain. To stop the galaxies flying apart, astronomers postulate that they sit in a spherical halo of dark matter.

M31

Andromeda's halo

Although a galaxy's halo is thought to be composed mostly of dark matter, there are also normal celestial objects residing here. This image shows some of the celestial objects in the Andromeda Galaxy's halo, including a globular cluster towards the bottom of the image. Most of these objects are stars but their combined mass is insufficient to solve the missing mass problem. There are several galaxies in the image as well, but these are very far away from M31.

EVIDENCE FOR DARK MATTER

Backwards spiral arm points to dark matter

NGC 4622 is an extremely rare galaxy. At first sight it might appear to be a normal spiral, but looks can be deceiving. Inside the two outer arms, a third arm is pointing the opposite way round. Astronomers call this a leading spiral arm and there is only one other galaxy known to possess one.

We have been able to produce such leading spiral arms in computer simulations where a small galaxy ploughs into a much larger galaxy. The smaller galaxy must be travelling in the opposite direction from the rotation of the larger galaxy and creates a density wave that triggers star formation in a forward-pointing spiral pattern. Most interestingly, the leading spiral arms are predicted to fade away quickly unless the whole galaxy is surrounded by a large mass of matter. The gravity of this mass stabilizes the arm. So the leading spiral arm in NGC 4622 is another piece of circumstantial evidence that some form of invisible dark matter dominates that galaxy.

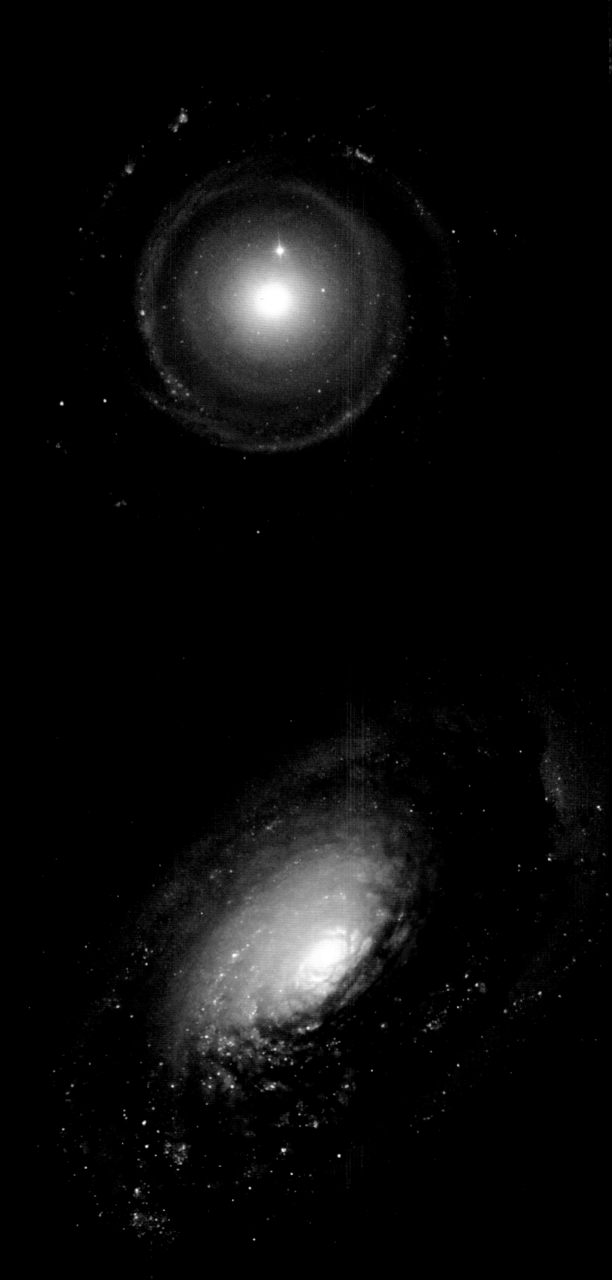

M64

Black Eye Galaxy

Through smaller optical telescopes the prominent dust cloud makes it look as though M64 has a huge black eye – hence its name. The 'injury' was caused by a collision with a much smaller galaxy. Nothing now exists of the colliding galaxy except the gigantic cloud of dust that obscures the front of the combined galaxy. Buried in the dust is a leading spiral arm, only the second one found in the universe.

DARK MATTER HALOS

DARK MATTER MAP

The Milky Way's halo

If you could remove all the ordinary matter from the Milky Way, and magically build a telescope that can see dark matter, then the view below might greet you. This super-computer simulation shows the accumulation of dark matter that holds the Milky Way together. Billions of years of cosmic history were simulated from an initially uniform distribution of dark matter. In that time, the dark matter fragmented into clumps as gravity pulled it together.

The central concentration is the halo in which the visible section of our galaxy resides. Beyond this, the distribution of dark matter in the extended halo is not smooth; instead it fragments into 10,000 clumps. The 120 largest of these should host dwarf galaxies, similar to the Magellanic Clouds. In reality, however, only 15 or so dwarf galaxies are known to exist around the Milky Way. This discrepancy between theory and observation is currently unexplained. It either signals a problem with dark matter theory or suggests that not every dark matter halo clump hosts a dwarf galaxy. Or perhaps there are many dim dwarf galaxies yet to be found around the Milky Way.

GAMMA-RAY MAP

Dark matter annihilations

One of the best candidates for dark matter is a theoretical particle called the neutralino. If this exists it offers a way to see dark matter because, whenever two neutralinos collide, they will transform into a pair of gamma rays. If our prediction of the clumped dark matter halo around the Milky Way is correct, dark matter collisions should generate a number of faint patches of gamma rays across the sky.

This colour-coded simulation shows what the next generation of more sensitive gamma ray telescopes might be able to see, if the neutralino interpretation of dark matter is the correct one. The yellow patches are the brightest gamma ray signals and correspond to the clumps of dark matter. The one in middle of the image is the centre of our g

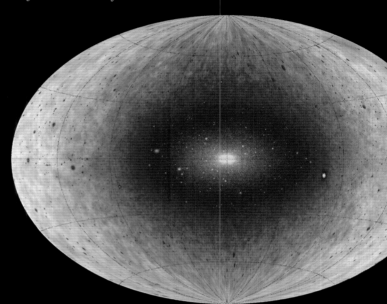

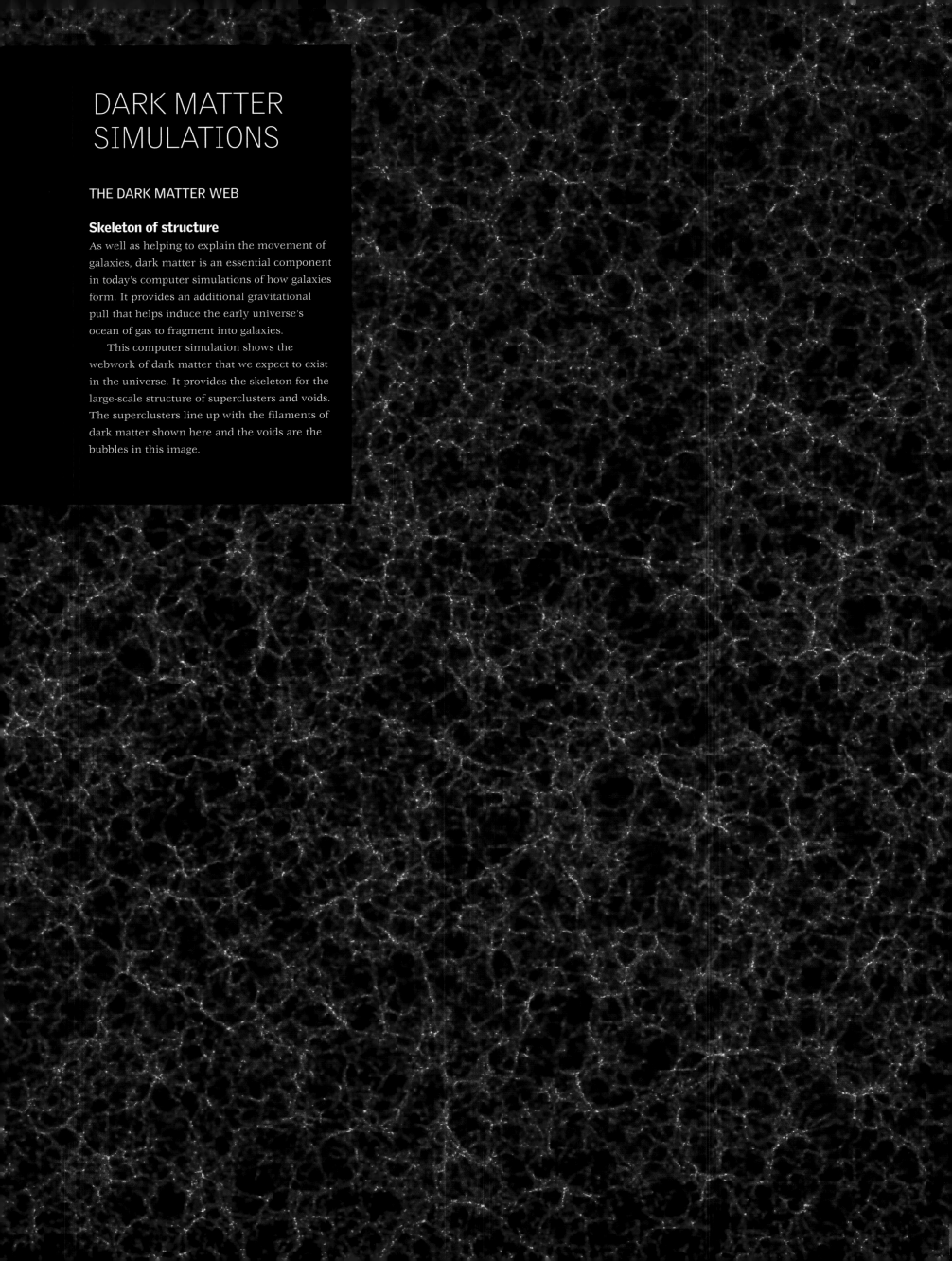

DARK MATTER SIMULATIONS

THE DARK MATTER WEB

Skeleton of structure

As well as helping to explain the movement of galaxies, dark matter is an essential component in today's computer simulations of how galaxies form. It provides an additional gravitational pull that helps induce the early universe's ocean of gas to fragment into galaxies.

This computer simulation shows the webwork of dark matter that we expect to exist in the universe. It provides the skeleton for the large-scale structure of superclusters and voids. The superclusters line up with the filaments of dark matter shown here and the voids are the bubbles in this image.

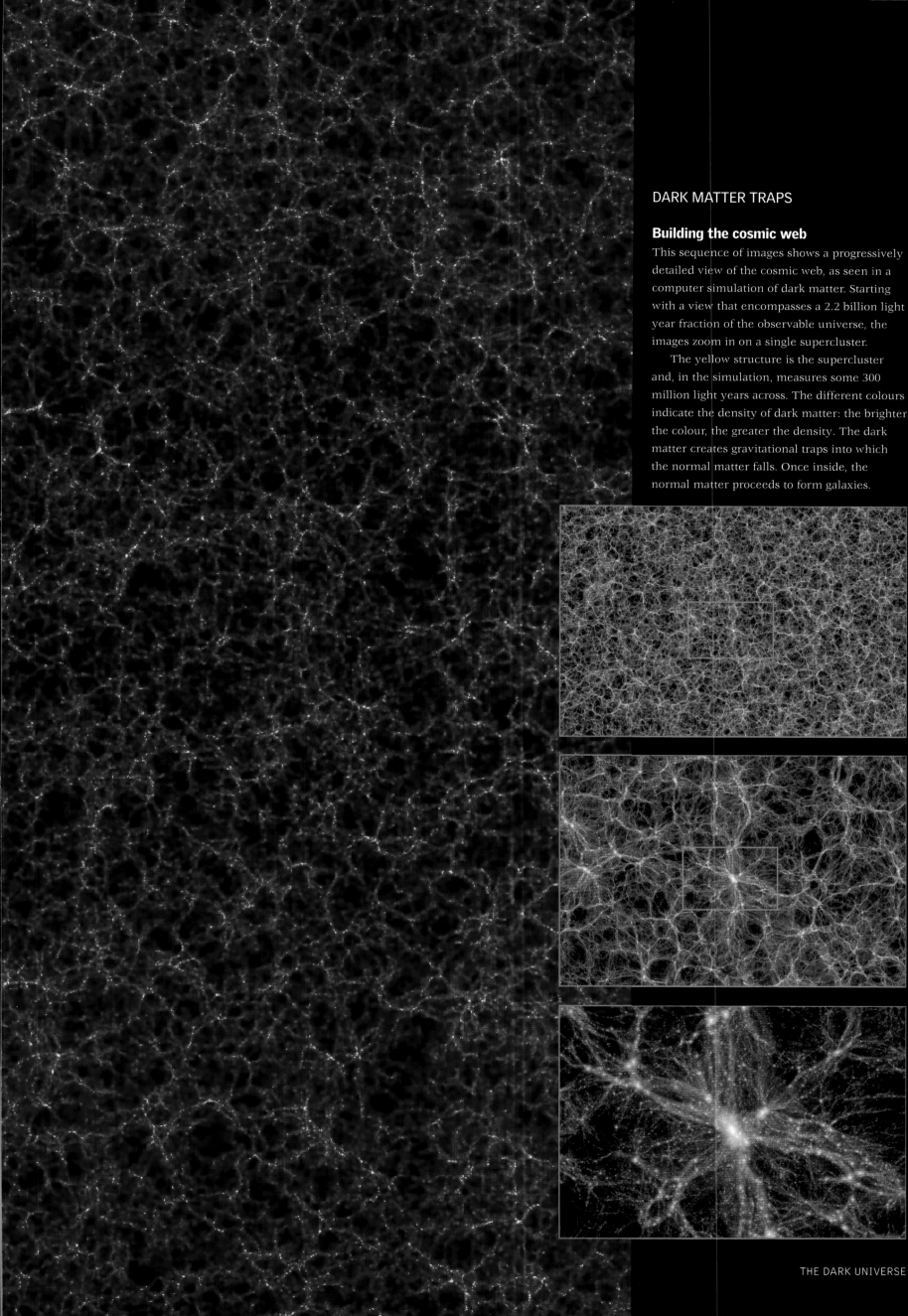

DARK MATTER TRAPS

Building the cosmic web

This sequence of images shows a progressively detailed view of the cosmic web, as seen in a computer simulation of dark matter. Starting with a view that encompasses a 2.2 billion light year fraction of the observable universe, the images zoom in on a single supercluster.

The yellow structure is the supercluster and, in the simulation, measures some 300 million light years across. The different colours indicate the density of dark matter: the brighter the colour, the greater the density. The dark matter creates gravitational traps into which the normal matter falls. Once inside, the normal matter proceeds to form galaxies.

MAPPING DARK MATTER

EAK GRAVITATIONAL LENSING

eflected light

suming that dark matter actually exists, we
n use the technique of gravitational lensing
map out its distribution across the universe
e Chapter 5). Whenever light rays from a
laxy pass close to another mass, whether it is
other galaxy or a cloud of dark matter, they
e slightly deflected. When viewed from the
rth the deflections cause distortions to
pear in the images of far distant galaxies.

By studying the distortions, we can gain an
idea of the path that the light must have taken
and so build an approximate map of the distribution of matter it has encountered on its
journey. This computer simulation shows
exaggerated light paths (in yellow) from
galaxies (yellow ovals) situated one billion light
years away, as they travel through the cosmic
web of dark matter (shown in red).

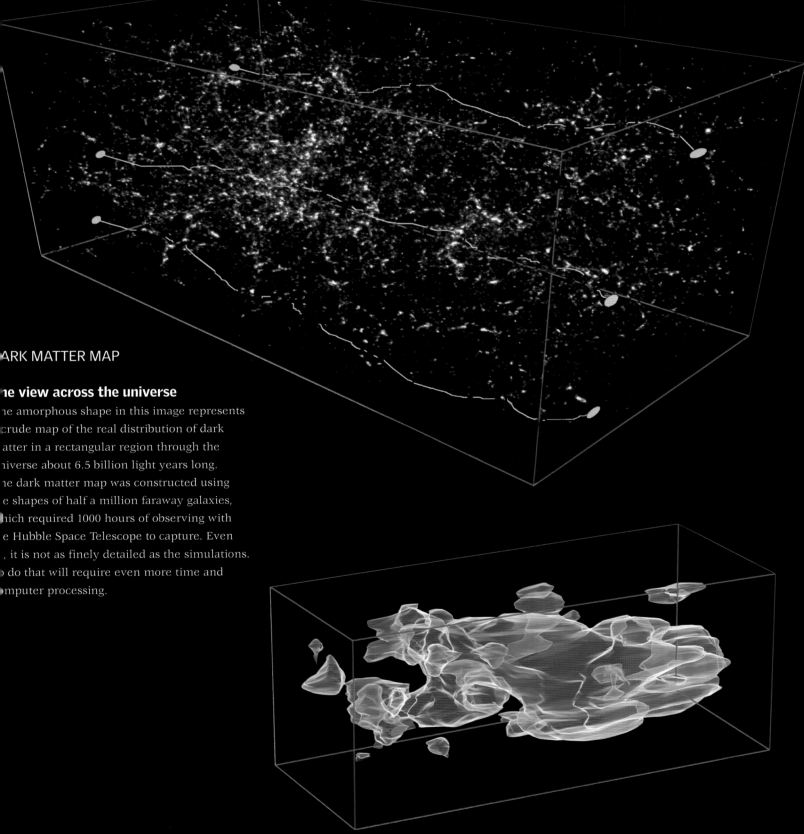

ARK MATTER MAP

he view across the universe

he amorphous shape in this image represents
crude map of the real distribution of dark
atter in a rectangular region through the
niverse about 6.5 billion light years long.
he dark matter map was constructed using
e shapes of half a million faraway galaxies,
hich required 1000 hours of observing with
e Hubble Space Telescope to capture. Even
, it is not as finely detailed as the simulations.
do that will require even more time and
mputer processing.

WHAT IF THERE IS NO DARK MATTER?

Bullet Cluster

Weak gravitational lensing can be used to reveal the location of dark matter in galaxy clusters, because the hypothetical substance appears to outweigh normal matter by at least ten times. Of the normal matter in such a cluster, most of it is thought to be in the form of hot gas surrounding the galaxies.

This composite image shows the galaxy cluster 1E 0657-556. Referred to as the Bullet Cluster, it is the product of collision between two large clusters of galaxies. Hot gas shining at X-ray wavelengths is depicted as two red clumps. The bullet-shaped one on the right shows the hot gas from the smaller cluster that passed through the hot gas from the other, larger one during the collision. The blue areas in the image depict where weak gravitational lenses show the majority of mass to be.

Most astronomers interpret this image as showing that the dark matter from each cluster has passed straight through the other. But what is the explanation if dark matter does not exist? In that case, it shows the locations in the universe where general relativity fails to explain the amount of gravity we observe and suggests that extremely weak gravitational fields do not behave in the ways predicted by Isaac Newton and Albert Einstein.

Cosmic smash-up

This simulation shows the sequence of events most astronomers believe took place in the Bullet Cluster. Blue represents the dark matter and red the hot gas in the galaxy cluster. As the collision takes place, the dark matter passes through unscathed but the hot gas interacts and it is dragged out of the cluster.

A CLUSTER RING

Cl0024+17

Surprising dark matter

A surprising discovery was made by studying the weak gravitational lensing around the galaxy cluster Cl0024+17, and using it to plot where the mass is concentrated. Instead of finding the dark matter inside the galaxy cluster, it appears to surround the cluster in a ring. The location of the inferred dark matter is shown in blue, superimposed over the optical picture of the cluster.

The cluster is 5 billion light years from Earth and the ring measures 2.6 million light years across. The separation of the dark matter from the normal matter is highly unusual and runs against what astronomers expected. It was always assumed that dark matter produced the gravitational well into which normal matter fell.

One possible solution is that, between one and two billion years ago, this cluster collided with another cluster of galaxies and somehow this has caused the dark matter to spread out and form the ring-like structure. If so, it would provide more evidence for dark matter's existence.

beyond dark matter, there is the new mystery of dark energy. This is the name for an unknown 'something' that permeates the universe and causes its expansion rate to accelerate. Previously, astronomers had expected the expansion to slow with time.

Supernovae provide excellent probes of the universe's expansion rate because they can be seen across billions of light years. The only trouble is that astronomers never know where or when they will explode, so we have to keep surveying the sky, ready to pounce when one does light up.

Here a supernova is pinpointed in the nearby galaxy M51 (below). At just 37 million light years, this galaxy is too close to show the influence of dark energy. As cosmic distances increase, however, the dark energy exerts more and more influence, gradually becoming dominant and forcing the universe's expansion to run faster.

BEFORE SUPERNOVA
January 21, 2005

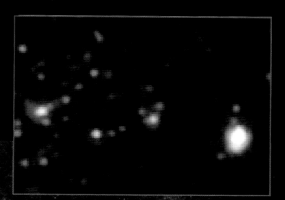

AFTER SUPERNOVA
July 11, 2005

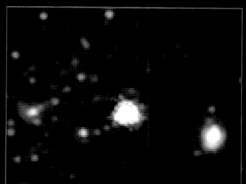

DISTANT SUPERNOVAE

Spotting the explosions

Astronomers now maintain a constant vigil for
supernovae in the distant universe. As each
one flares, it briefly gives out as much light as
all the rest of the stars in its galaxy combined.
With each new supernova discovered, we
harvest some more information about the
acceleration of the universe. Each of these
galaxies and its respective supernova (below)
are billions of light years away.

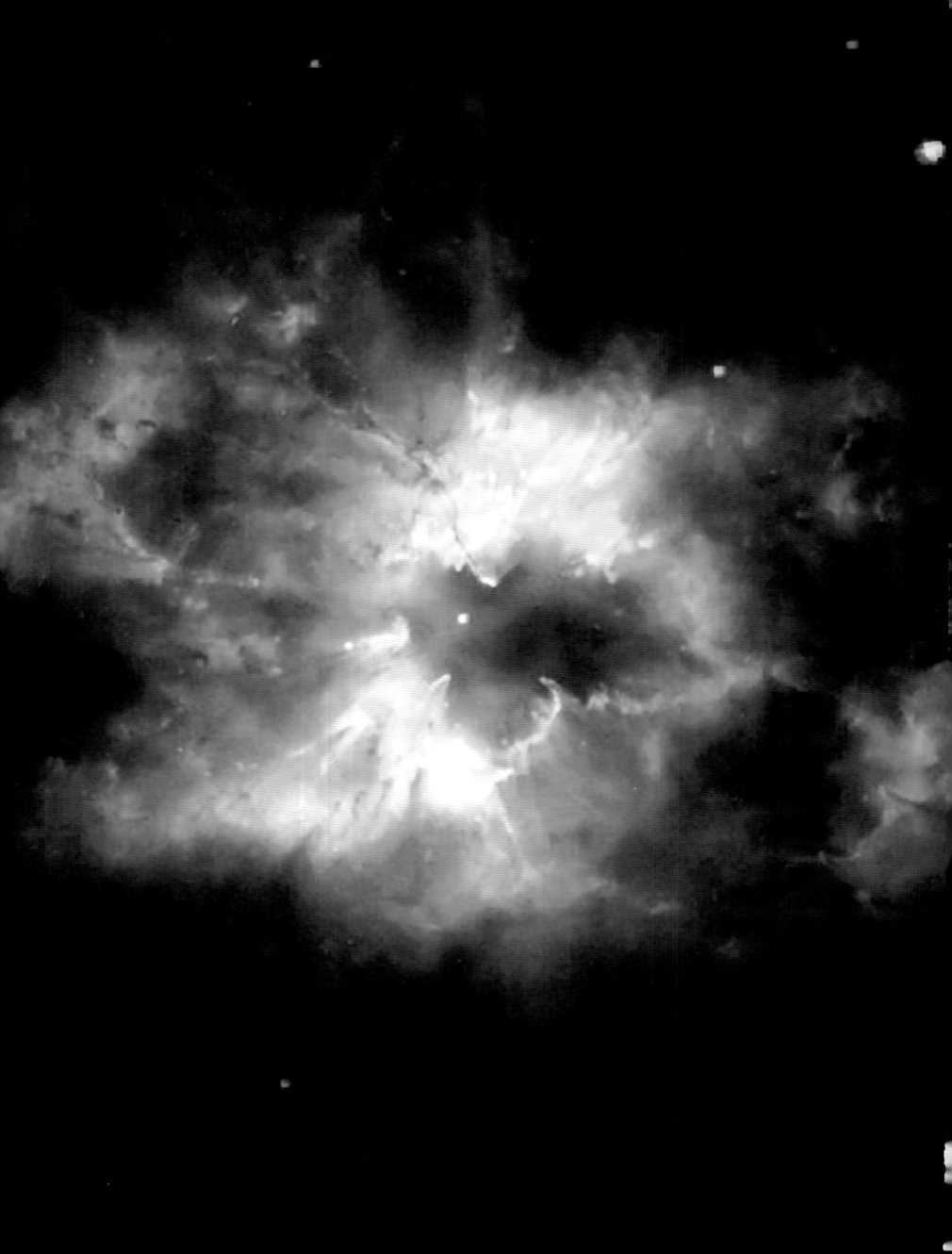

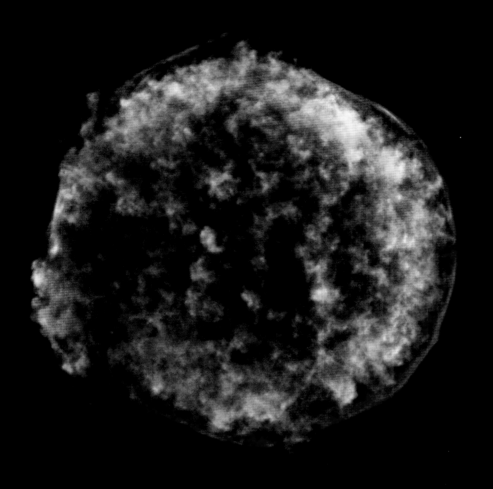

SNR1572

Tycho's supernova remnant

This is all that remains of a white dwarf that was seen to explode as a Type Ia supernova on 11 November 1572. The astronomer Tycho Brahe witnessed its demise. During the intervening centuries, the debris has expanded to become this cloud, some 20 light years across. Even today, the cloud continues to expand, tearing through space at 25 million kilometres per hour (15 million mph).

SIRIUS A AND B

Supernova in the making?

Sirius B is a white dwarf star in orbit around a more normal star, Sirius A. The distance separating the two stars is about the same as the distance separating the planet Uranus from our Sun. Had the two stars been closer it is possible that, as Sirius A expands to become a red giant star in later life, it would have funnelled matter onto Sirius B and created a Type Ia supernova on our cosmic doorstep. Sirius is only 8.6 light years away and the resulting blast of radiation could have had dire consequences for the life on Earth. Thankfully, the separation between Sirius A and B means that this is unlikely to happen.

THE BEST SUPERNOVAE

NGC 2440

White dwarf

In the search for distant supernovae to reveal the accelerating universe, we are always on the lookout for one particular type of exploding star, called a Type Ia supernova. These are the stellar explosions caused when the dense core of a dying star, such as the one shown here in the centre of NGC 2440, attracts gas from a nearby star and buckles under the weight of the new material. A study of various supernovae of Type Ia, conducted by two independent teams, revealed the expanding universe because the supernovae were dimmer than expected.

The surrounding gas in this image was once the outer layer of this star. The dense core is known as a white dwarf star.

BREAKING THE SUPERCLUSTERS APART

VIRGO CLUSTER

The demise of the Local Supercluster

We do not yet know how dark energy will change with time. It might simply be a constant quantity and the expansion of the universe will continue to accelerate at a steady pace. In this case, the Virgo Cluster, our nearest large cluster of galaxies, will be driven further away from us at an ever increasing rate. The action of the dark energy will be to stretch out the Local Supercluster until, eventually, the feeling of association between the various clusters and groups that comprise this structure will be lost.

The same fate will be suffered by all the superclusters, leading to a more diffuse collection of clusters and groups throughout the universe.

SMALL MAGELLANIC CLOUD

The destruction of the Local Group

If dark energy gradually builds in strength, the Local Group of galaxies could be ripped apart. At present the 40 galaxies are huddled together and the force of their mutual gravity is strong enough to overcome the expansion of the universe. If the dark energy increases, accelerating this expansion, then the galaxies of the Local Group could be forced apart. In an extreme case, the Magellanic Clouds could be ripped from their orbits around the Milky Way. Eventually the Milky Way might end up as a single galaxy floating in an enormous dark-energy fuelled void.

THE BIG RIP

CASSIOPEIA A

How strong are black holes?

The possibility exists that dark energy might accelerate the universe at ever increasing rates until eventually it became so strong that it would drive apart the stars in the Milky Way. And the disruption would not stop there. Dark energy would grow ever stronger, ripping apart stars and planets and eventually even atoms. We call this nightmare scenario the big rip.

But what of the black holes such as those created when stars explode? At the centre of Cassiopeia A, we have found what might be a black hole, hungrily devouring gas. Black holes are supposedly the ultimate gravitational forces in the universe, yet calculations show that phantom energy, as this particularly virulent form of dark energy is called, will dissolve black holes like tablets in a glass of water and then rip apart whatever particles the black hole residue becomes.

MS0735.6+7421

Supermassive black holes

Not even the supermassive black holes at the centre of active galaxies are immune to the unstoppable force of phantom energy. This is the galaxy cluster MS0735.6+7421. It is home to around 50 galaxies, each possessing a supermassive black hole. The central galaxy hosts a large black hole that squirts two jets (in red) off into space. These have carved holes (shown as clear regions in the blue, colour-coded gas) that are seven times wider than the entire Milky Way Galaxy. In the process, the jets have displaced a trillion tonnes of gas. Yet even the billion solar mass black hole responsible for this cataclysm will present no obstacle to the phantom energy's destructive force. It will be ripped apart like tissue paper.

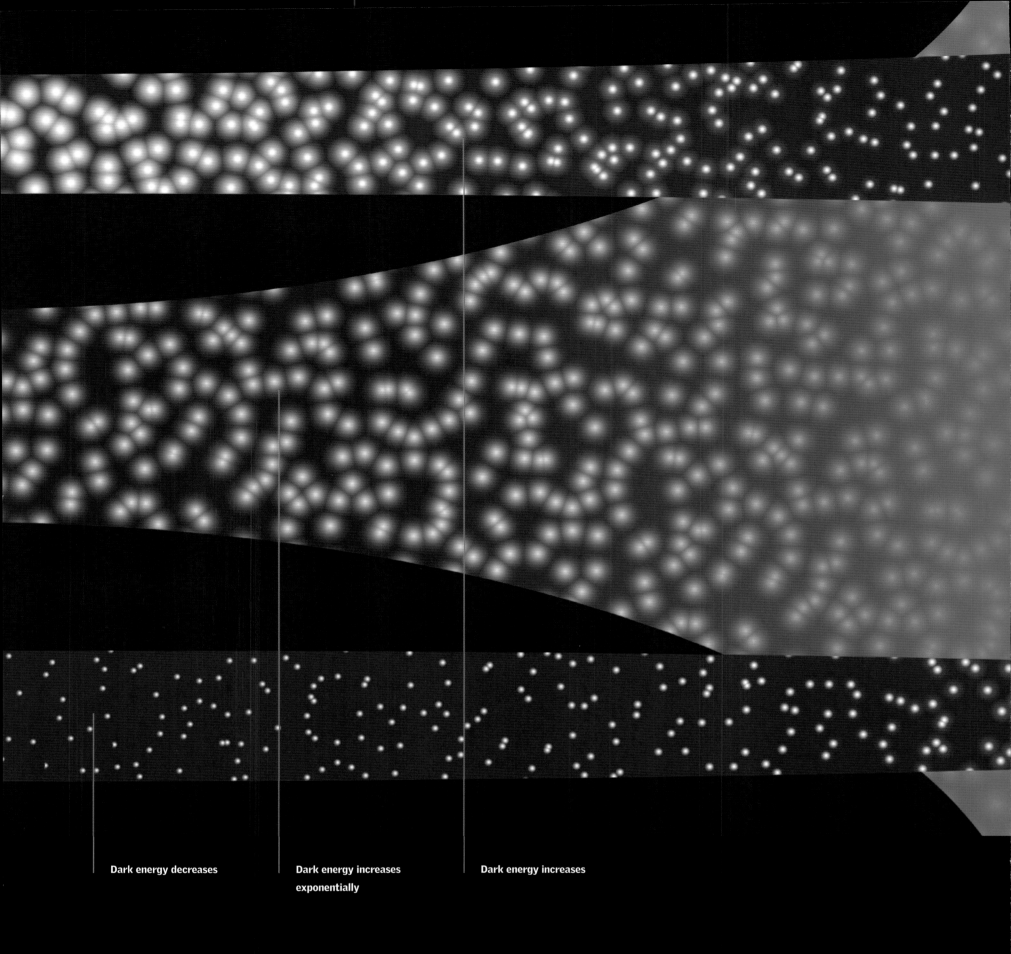

Dark energy decreases

Dark energy increases exponentially

Dark energy increases

ALL POSSIBLE FUTURES

THE FATE OF THE UNIVERSE

Dominant dark energy

Cosmologists now identify three possible fates for the universe. The first will happen if the dark energy remains constant or increases a little. This will drive superclusters apart and then, depending upon the exact strength of the dark energy, could also destroy clusters. The worst-case scenario, the second option, is the big rip in which dark energy increases so quickly that it literally tears the universe to pieces.

Finally there is a faint possibility that the dark energy might not increase but decline and reverse its direction. In this case, it would augment the force of gravity and actually reverse the expansion of the universe.

In this case, space would begin shrinking and the galaxies would eventually collide, merging into super galaxies. Stars would become packed ever more closely together so that they would regularly collide. At the centre

of each super galaxy, supermassive black holes will also come together, each titanic collision setting the fabric of space rippling. Eventually the universe would disappear into itself, in a rerun of the big bang, only moving in reverse.

At present, all scenarios are possible. The true fate of the universe can only be determined through more study and observation.

Glossary

Absolute zero

The lowest temperature attainable in the universe, equivalent to $-273\,°C$ ($-459\,°F$), known as zero kelvin. Essentially, this is the temperature at which atoms cease all movement, even vibration. There is no upper limit on temperature.

Accretion disc

A disc of dust and gas formed as material spirals down into the gravitational field of a body, such as a forming star or a black hole.

Active Galactic Nucleus (AGN)

The core of an active galaxy. The energy generated in an AGN can outshine all the other stars in that galaxy. There is now persuasive evidence that an AGN is powered by the heating of an accretion disc as it spirals into a supermassive black hole.

Active galaxy

A galaxy that emits more energy from its centre than can be accounted for by its normal components: stars, dust and gas.

Background radiation *see* Cosmic Microwave Background Radiation.

Big bang

The event in which the universe came into existence and began expanding. Modern estimates place this event at 13.7 billion years ago.

Black hole

A dense celestial object with a gravitational field so strong that, within a certain radius, known

Brown dwarf

A failed star, containing less than eight percent of the Sun's mass. Unable to sustain the nuclear fusion of hydrogen atoms, brown dwarfs probably look like giant versions of the planet Jupiter.

Cepheid variable

A type of variable star that undergoes cyclic changes in its brightness, closely related to its average luminosity. By measuring the periods of variation in Cepheids in distant galaxies, astronomers can estimate their true luminosities and then calculate their distances.

Comet

A chunk of dust and ice left over from the formation of a planetary system. Comets in the solar system are classified according to their orbital period. Short-period comets complete their orbit in less than 200 years, while long-period comets can take millions of years.

Cosmic Microwave Background Radiation

A faint glow of microwave radiation across the entire sky. It is believed to be the afterglow of the big bang itself, now cooled to below $-270\,°C$ ($-454\,°F$), just $2.7\,°C$ ($4.9\,°F$) above absolute zero.

Dark ages

The time between 300,000 years and approximately 1 billion years when the first celestial objects were forming. Before these objects existed there was no light in the universe.

Dark energy

A hypothetical form of energy thought to permeate all of space, creating one dominant

Doppler effect

A natural phenomenon in which the perceived wavelength and frequency of waves received from an object are affected by the relative movement of the emitter and receiver. When the emitter and receiver are moving towards one another, the received wavelength is squashed and the frequency driven higher. When they are separating, the wavelength is stretched and the frequency lowered.

Doppler shift

The shift in the frequency of a wave caused by the Doppler effect. In everyday life, Doppler shifts are often audible in the sirens of passing emergency vehicles, but astronomers are most interested in the Doppler shifts of light, since they reveal the motion of astronomical objects relatively to us. *See also* Redshift.

Dwarf galaxy

A small, faint galaxy, either irregular or elliptical in structure.

Einstein ring

A gravitational lens in which the alignment is so perfect that the background object is transformed into a ring surrounding the lensing object.

Electromagnetic radiation

A form of energy that propagates across the universe as a combination of electrical and magnetic waves. The most familiar form is visible light, whose colours correspond to different wavelengths and energies. The full electromagnetic spectrum runs from extremely energetic gamma rays, via X-rays, ultraviolet,

Event horizon
The point of no return around a black hole. Anything crossing this boundary will be forever cut off from the rest of the universe.

Fusion *see* Nuclear fusion.

Galactic halo
A spherical region around a spiral galaxy that contains dim stars and globular clusters. The radius of the halo surrounding the Milky Way extends some 50,000 light years from the galactic centre. It is also thought to contain dark matter.

Galaxy
A gravitationally bound system of dust, gas and stars. Galaxies range in size from a few hundred, to hundreds of thousands of light years across, and are classified according to their appearance. The most common types are spiral, barred spiral, elliptical, lenticular and irregular.

Galaxy cluster
A collection of hundreds to thousands of galaxies bound together by gravity.

Galaxy supercluster
A grouping of perhaps a dozen or more neighbouring galaxy clusters.

Gamma ray
The most energetic form of electromagnetic radiation.

Gamma ray burst
A brief but immensely powerful burst (measured in minutes at most) of gamma rays from space. Believed to be triggered by hypernovae, or the collisions between neutron stars or between black holes.

General relativity
Albert Einstein's theory that explains gravity as a distortion of space and time.

Globular cluster
A distinct, densely packed ball of stars in orbit around a central galaxy.

Gravitational lens
A massive object that magnifies or distorts the light from objects lying behind it. *See also* Einstein ring.

Gravity
A physical force that appears to exert a mutual attraction between all masses, governed by the mass of the objects and the distance between them. *See also* General relativity.

Herbig–Haro object
A type of emission nebula created by jets of material ejected by newborn stars colliding with the interstellar medium.

Hubble constant
A measure of the rate at which the universe is expanding, in kilometres per second per megaparsec (a megaparsec is roughly 3.26 million light years).

Hubble tuning fork diagram
A diagram on which Edwin Hubble classified the different types of galaxy. Originally Hubble thought it was an evolutionary sequence but this is now known to be false.

Hypernova
An unusually powerful type of supernova, associated with the demise of particularly massive stars that only existed in the early days of the universe.

Index Catalogue (IC)
A two-part supplement, published in 1895 and 1908, adding 5386 astronomical objects to the New General Catalogue (NGC).

Infrared radiation
A section of the electromagnetic spectrum invisible to human eyes but sensed as heat or thermal radiation.

Inflation
An event just after the big bang in which, for a fraction of a second, the entire universe was driven to expand much faster than normal.

Interstellar medium
The extremely rarefied material scattered through the space between the stars, typically consisting of 90 percent hydrogen, 9 percent helium and 1 percent dust.

Ionization
The process that produces ions – atoms that are electrically charged by the capture or loss of electrons. Atoms can be stripped of their electrons by high-energy radiation (from stars, for example). Material that has been completely ionized is known as plasma.

Irregular galaxy
Any galaxy that lacks the necessary structures to be classified as an elliptical, spiral or lenticular galaxy. Despite their lack of form, irregular galaxies are typically rich in gas, dust, and young stars.

Lenticular galaxy
A galaxy that resembles a spiral galaxy, with a central nucleus and a disc, but without spiral arms.

Light
The electromagnetic radiation detectable to the human eye. However, the term is loosely applied to other forms of electromagnetic radiation, especially in the ultraviolet and infrared regions of the spectrum.

Light hour
The distance travelled by light in a vacuum during one hour: 1 billion km (620 million miles).

Light minute
The distance travelled by light in a vacuum during one minute: 17.9 million km (11.1 million miles).

Light second
The distance travelled by light in a vacuum during one second: 299,792 km (186,282 miles).

Light year
The distance travelled by light in a vacuum during one year: 9.5 trillion km (5.9 trillion miles).

Local Group
A collection of approximately 40 galaxies spread over 10 million light years, dominated by our own Milky Way and the Andromeda Galaxy.

Look-back time
The time difference associated with looking at a distant object, due to the finite speed of light. Look-back time is just an interesting curiosity within our cosmic neighbourhood, but on the largest scales, when it amounts to billions of years, it reveals the universe in a significantly earlier stage of its development.

Magellanic Clouds
Two nearby irregular galaxies that appear to be in orbit around the Milky Way.

Mass
A measure of the amount of matter in a body. In astronomy, there is a careful distinction between mass and weight – weight is the force acting on an object with mass in a gravitational field.

Messier Catalogue (M)
A list of about 100 nebulous-looking astronomical objects compiled by French astronomer Charles Messier between 1758 and 1781. Most were later identified as galaxies or gaseous nebulae; a few as star clusters.

Milky Way

Our galaxy: the name is derived from our perception of it as a misty band of stars that divides the night sky. The Milky Way is, in fact, a large barred spiral galaxy spanning 100,000 light years and containing around 200 billion stars. Our solar system lies about two-thirds of the way towards the edge of its disc, in a truncated spiral arm.

Molecular cloud

An accumulation of dust and gas that is significantly denser than the interstellar medium. Such clouds can span hundreds of light years and are the sites of star formation.

Nebula

A cloud of dust and gas in space. See also Emission nebula, Molecular cloud, Planetary nebula.

Neutron star

An extremely dense stellar remnant produced in a supernova explosion when huge gravitational forces compress electrons and protons to produce neutrons.

New General Catalogue (NGC)

A compilation of 7800 astronomical objects published in 1888 by John L.E. Dreyer and based on earlier observations made by William and John Herschel.

Nuclear fusion

The process that powers stars. Two or more atomic nuclei are forced together, forming a single larger nucleus and releasing energy. Most stars spend the majority of their lives converting hydrogen into helium. Red giant stars are fusing heavier elements.

Observable universe

That part of the universe that we are able to study, limited by look-back time to a sphere of space 13.7 billion light years in radius and centred on our own location. At the edge of the observable universe in every direction, we are looking back to around 300,000 years after the big bang itself.

Open star cluster

A group of young stellar siblings, born from the same molecular cloud but only loosely bound together by gravity. Such clusters are usually dominated by short-lived brilliant blue stars, but are fated to disperse over a period of several hundred million years.

Orbit

The trajectory of one celestial body around another.

Photon

A particle of light; the quantum (smallest possible) unit of the electromagnetic force.

Planet

An object that orbits a star. By historical accident, the name is reserved for large bodies, but there is controversy over where the definition of a planet should end. Pluto has recently been reclassified as a dwarf planet.

Planetary nebula

A luminous shell of debris surrounding a dying star, flung into space as a red giant nears the final stages of its life and becomes unstable. Planetary nebulae are transitory phenomena lasting no more than 100,000 years – fading as their central white dwarfs cool. The name originates from their resemblance to planets when viewed through early telescopes.

Pulsar

A rotating neutron star that emits a sweeping beam of high-energy radiation from its magnetic poles.

Quasar

The very bright, far distant core of an extremely powerful active galaxy. The name is derived from 'quasi-stellar radio source' – so-called because this class of object was first identified through its radio emissions.

Radiation

The transmission of energy or matter. See also Electromagnetic radiation.

Radiation pressure

The pressure exerted on an object by a stream of photons; it sculpts gas clouds in space.

Radio galaxy

A type of active galaxy, usually elliptical, that emits large quantities of radio waves. Often this radiation is in the form of jets from the centre of the galaxy that create vast clouds of radio emission on either side of the galaxy, hundreds of thousands of light years across.

Red dwarf

A small and relatively cool star with a diameter and mass of less than one-third that of the Sun. Red dwarfs comprise the vast majority of stars.

Red giant

An ageing star that has exhausted all the hydrogen in its core and is first supported by a thin spherical shell of hydrogen fusion around the core and, later, the fusion of heavier elements within the core. This change of processes boosts the star's brightness, but also causes it to balloon in size, allowing its surface to cool and turn red.

Redshift

A Doppler shift in light created when the distance between Earth and the light source is increasing. The opposite effect, when distance is decreasing, is a blueshift. Both are useful for measuring the relative motions of stars, but redshift is particularly important for measuring the overall expansion of the universe. Redshifts and blueshifts can be precisely measured using spectral lines.

Ring galaxy

A galaxy surrounded by a distinct ring of bright stars. It is thought they form when spiral galaxies are disrupted by a head-on collision with another galaxy.

Sagittarius A*

The supermassive black hole at the centre of the Milky Way.

Seyfert galaxy

A spiral galaxy with an unusually bright core that is caused by the activity around a central supermassive black hole. Seyfert galaxies are a type of active galaxy.

Solar mass

A measure used to express the mass of stars and larger objects. It is equal to the mass of our Sun, or 1.98 trillion trillion tonnes.

Spectroscopy

The recording and study of light split into a spectrum, often concentrating on the location and identification of particular spectral lines that indicate certain elements or molecules within, for example, a star's atmosphere.

Spectrum

The light from an astronomical object, split up into a long band of different wavelengths and colours. Traditionally, a spectrum was formed using a glass prism that bent light of different colours by different amounts. Today, astronomers use diffraction gratings – finely scored 'windows' that bend the light more effectively and absorb less of it.

Spiral galaxy
A galaxy with a spherical central bulge of older stars, surrounded by a flattened disc containing a spiral pattern of young, hot stars. The Milky Way is a spiral galaxy.

Star
A massive ball of hydrogen and helium bound together by gravity and shining for most of its life with the light of nuclear fusion. Stars are born in nebulae and open clusters, and spend most of their lives fusing hydrogen into helium, a state known as 'main sequence', before evolving into red giants and, depending on their mass, dying as planetary nebulae or supernovae. The stellar remnants they leave behind may be white dwarfs, neutron stars or black holes.

Starburst galaxy
A galaxy (often irregular in structure) experiencing an intense burst of star formation. Most starbursts are triggered by interaction – or even collision – with another galaxy.

Stellar wind
A stream of particles emanating from a star.

Sun
The star at the centre of our solar system.

Supergiant
An extremely massive star that has exhausted the supply of hydrogen in its core, increased in luminosity as it enters a phase equivalent to a red giant, and ballooned in size. While the expansion of Sun-like stars means their surfaces cool down to become red or orange, some supergiants produce so much energy that their surface remains hot, and they can have almost any colour.

Supermassive black hole
A black hole with a mass of millions or billions of solar masses. Most, if not all, galaxies are thought to harbour a supermassive black hole at their core.

Supernova
The explosive demise of a star. Supernovae come in two types: Type I and Type II. A Type I supernova involves the collapse of an existing white dwarf; a Type II supernova is the explosion that marks the demise of a star of eight solar masses or more. Depending on the mass of the star, either a neutron star or a black hole is left at the centre of the conflagration.

Supernova remnant
An expanding shell of dust and gas – the deb of a supernova explosion, mixed together w swept-up interstellar matter.

Ultraviolet radiation
Electromagnetic radiation with a shorter wavelength than violet light.

Universe
The entirety of space, time and everything t it contains. *See also* Observable universe.

White dwarf
The dense, cooling ember of a star that has exhausted its nuclear fuel and collapsed und the force of its own gravity. White dwarfdom awaits all but the most massive stars.

Wolf–Rayet star
A particularly massive, short-lived star, usua containing more than 25 solar masses of material. Wolf–Rayets have powerful stellar winds that strip away the outer layers of the own atmospheres, leaving their interiors exposed.

X-rays
High-energy electromagnetic radiation. Less energetic than gamma rays, but more so tha ultraviolet radiation.

Index

A

1E 0657-556, 235
2MASS, 220-1
3C31, 135
3C75, 207
3C272.1, 135
3C296, 135
Abell 400, 207
Abell 1689, 122-3
Abell 2667, 216-17
Abell 3627, 74-5
Abell S0740, 214
absolute zero, 248
accretion disc, 127, 248
active galactic nucleus (AGN), 138, 198, 248
active galaxies, 12, 124-43, 201, 248
AE Aurigae, 58-9
Alpha Centauri, 49
AM 0644-741, 202
Andromeda Galaxy, 7, 42-3, 92-3, 210, 212, 229
Ant Nebula, 61
Antennae Galaxies, 116-17, 190-1
Arp 220, 203

B

background radiation, 91, 103, 222-3, 227, 248
Barnard 68, 108
Barnard's Galaxy, 213
barred spiral galaxies, 10, 12-13, 26-9, 186
BD + 602522, 157
Big Bang, 88-103, 144, 148, 150, 188, 246, 248
Big Dipper, 14
Black Eye Galaxy, 230
black holes, 29, 36, 38, 39, 69, 117, 124-43, 147,
    156, 172, 201, 207, 245, 248
blazars, 127, 138
blue stragglers, 203
blue supergiant, 38, 248
Bode's Galaxy, 112
Bok globules, 109, 150, 248
Boomerang Nebula, 60
brown dwarf stars, 57, 174, 248
Bubble Nebula, 157
Bullet Cluster, 235

C

Carina Nebula, 46-7, 156, 165
Cartwheel Galaxy, 35
Cassiopeia, 157
Cassiopeia A, 129, 244-5
Cat's Eye Nebula, 87
Centaurus A, 132-3
Cepheid variable stars, 72-3, 81, 82, 248
Cigar Galaxy, 112-13
Circinus Galaxy, 136
Cl0024 + 17, 236-7
Cloverleaf Quasar, 118-19
clusters, 12, 16, 30, 111, 122-3, 148,
    208-23, 210-21, 235, 237, 249

Coma Cluster, 210, 216
Comet Galaxy, 216
comets, 77, 248
Cone Nebula, 168
cosmic background radiation, 91, 102, 222-3,
    227, 248
cosmological distance ladder, 72-3
Crab Nebula, 62-3
Crab Pulsar, 63
curvature of space, 106-7, 126-7
Cygnus, 126
Cygnus A, 135
Cygnus Loop, 64
Cygnus X-1, 128

D

dark ages, 248
dark energy, 9, 227, 238-9, 242-7, 248
dark matter, 9, 36, 122, 224-47, 248
dark nebulae, 108
deep fields, 100, 248
Doppler effect, 90, 248
Doppler shift, 248
Dumbbell Nebula, 83
dwarf galaxies, 12, 14, 17, 32-3, 55, 184, 186,
    188-90, 193, 194, 196, 210, 216, 231, 248
dwarf planets, 179

E

Eagle Nebula, 48-9
Earth, 40, 180-1
Einstein, Albert, 90, 106, 226, 249
Einstein rings, 120-1, 248
electromagnetic radiation, 8, 69, 248
elliptical galaxies, 10, 12-13, 30-1, 38, 132, 134,
    141, 184, 248
emission nebulae, 52, 248
Enceladus, 179
ergosphere, 127
Eskimo Nebula, 61
ESO 97-G13, 136
ESO 172-07, 60
ESO 325-G004, 214
ESO 350-G40, 35
ESO 510-G13, 21, 193
Eta Carina, 46, 154, 155, 165
Europa, 181
event horizon, 126-7, 249

F

field galaxies, 211
flocculent spiral galaxies, 19
Fornax A, 134
Fornax cluster, 34, 195

G

galaxies, 6, 10-69, 91, 147, 208-27, 249
    active galaxies, 12, 124-143, 201, 248
    barred spiral galaxies, 10, 12-13, 26-9, 186

clusters, 12, 16, 30, 111, 122-3, 148,
    208-23, 210-21, 235, 237, 249
collisions, 14, 21, 30, 35, 39, 111, 115,
    116-17, 127, 132, 140, 142, 184-5, 190, 198,
    202, 203, 207, 226, 235, 246
dwarf galaxies, 12, 14, 17, 32-3, 55, 184, 186,
    188-90, 193, 194, 196, 210, 216, 231, 248
elliptical galaxies, 10, 12-13, 30-1, 38, 132,
    134, 141, 184, 248
evolution of, 184
field galaxies, 211
flocculent spiral galaxies, 19
galactic halo, 249
grand design spiral galaxies, 19, 26, 55
irregular galaxies, 10, 12-13, 32-4, 81, 195,
    201, 249
lenticular galaxies, 10, 12-13, 22-5, 249
radio galaxies, 127, 134, 140, 194, 250
ring galaxies, 10, 35, 202, 250
Seyfert galaxies, 125, 134, 136, 140, 250
spiral galaxies, 10, 12-13, 16-21, 38, 55, 73,
    86, 90, 132, 134, 136, 140, 185, 195, 201,
    230, 251
starburst galaxies, 112, 116, 148, 185, 190, 196
    207, 251
superclusters, 210, 231-2, 242, 246, 249
types of, 12
Galileo, 13
gamma ray bursts, 146, 172, 249
gamma rays, 147, 172, 231, 249
general relativity, 90, 106, 249
giant stars, 63, 154, 165
globular clusters, 78-9, 113, 160, 203, 214, 229,
    249
G0.15-0.05, 155
grand design spiral galaxies, 19, 26, 55
gravitational lenses, 118-19, 120-1, 122, 234,
    237, 249
gravitational waves, 107
gravity, 34, 38, 42, 63, 91, 92, 104-21, 126, 141,
    184, 208, 218, 222, 226-7, 249
GRB 990123, 172
Great Wall, 211

H

H1413 + 117, 118-19
halo, 39, 78, 229, 231, 248
HCG 87, 29, 110-11
HD 3651, 174
HDE 226868, 128
HE0450-2958, 137
HE1239-2426, 137
Helix Nebula, 83, 84-5
HEN-1357, 83
Herbig-Haro Objects, 249
HH32, 151
Hickson Compact Group 87, 110-11
Hoag's Object, 35
Hodge 301, 159

Photo credits

First published in Great Britain in 2008 by

Quercus Publishing Plc
21 Bloomsbury Square
London
WC1A 2NS

A CIP catalogue record for this book is available from the British
Library

ISBN 978 1 84724 405 5

Printed and bound in China

10 9 8 7 6 5 4 3 2 1

Design: Grade Design Consultants, www.gradedesign.com
Illustration: Jurgen Ziewe, www.3d-art.co.uk